After the holidays 1

1 Summer

a) Summer! What is important to you? Fill the fish with **your** summer words.

Tipp
Du kannst auch im *dictionary* im TB nachschlagen.

b) Look at the fish again. Put your words in groups like weather, sports, free time activities, places, … . Colour the fish that go together in one colour.

2 Summer poems

a) Summer is a wonderful time. Read the summer poems.

In summer	Blue sky	Mrs Summer
I see the sun	Yellow sun	She wears pink and green
I hear the sea	This is	She likes bees
I feel great	Summer fun	She hates rain
In summer		She is a flower
		That's Mrs Summer

b) Now write **your** summer poem.

In summer

I see _____

I hear _____

I feel _____

In summer

Mr Summer

He wears _____

He likes _____

He hates _____

He is a _____

That's Mr Summer

1 After the holidays

3 Emma's phone call

a) Emma is in Turkey. She calls her grandmother to tell her about her holidays. Fill in these words:

am   is   are

Tipp
I am = I'm.

Emma:	Hi Gran!
Grandmother:	Hello Emma, how _____ you?
Emma:	I _____ fine. The weather _____ good. It _____ warm and sunny. And the food _____ great. I have a kebab every day.
Grandmother:	_____ you brown already?
Emma:	Yes, we _____ very brown! We go to the beach every day. There _____ some English kids. They _____ really cool. One of the boys _____ from London, too. And one of the girls _____ from Manchester. She _____ very nice. We play volleyball at the beach. We _____ a good team. Yesterday we won a match.
Grandmother:	Well, Emma, that sounds great!
Emma:	Hey Gran, how _____ Bernie?
Grandmother:	Your hamster ____ fine. He had an apple today. He _____ always very hungry.
Emma:	OK. Give him a kiss from me! Ha ha, only joking. OK, bye, Grandma!
Grandmother:	Bye!

b) Now listen and check.

4 Back from the pony camp

Caroline had a lot of fun at the pony camp. There was a race on the last day. She tells Gillian everything about it. Listen to Caroline and put the pictures in the correct order.

  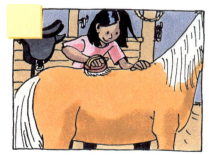

After the holidays 1

5 Thorpe Park

This is the website of Thorpe Park. Read it and tick ✔ the right answers.

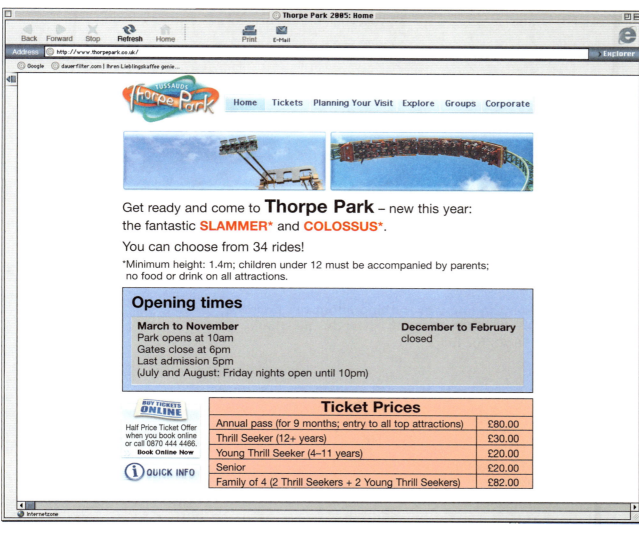

1. Um im *Slammer* zu fahren, muss man …
   - mindestens 1,40 m groß sein. ☐
   - mindestens 12 Jahre sein. ☐
   - immer mit seinen Eltern fahren. ☐

2. An einem Freitag im August hat Thorpe Park bis …
   - 17 Uhr geöffnet. ☐
   - bis 18 Uhr geöffnet. ☐
   - bis 22 Uhr geöffnet. ☐

3. Thorpe Park ist …
   - das ganze Jahr über geöffnet. ☐
   - von Dezember bis Februar geschlossen. ☐
   - am Freitag immer geschlossen. ☐

4. Eine Familie mit zwei Kindern zwischen 4 und 11 Jahren muss …
   - £80 Eintritt bezahlen. ☐
   - £82 Eintritt bezahlen. ☐
   - £100 Eintritt bezahlen. ☐

5. So oft kann man mit einem *Annual Pass* Thorpe Park besuchen:
   - jeden Freitag. ☐
   - 9-mal pro Jahr. ☐
   - neun Monate lang. ☐

6. Man bekommt Eintrittskarten um die Hälfte billiger, wenn man …
   - online bucht oder telefonisch bestellt. ☐
   - nur eine Stunde im Park bleibt. ☐
   - mit Kreditkarte bezahlt. ☐

1 After the holidays

6 Go or went?

Look at these sentences. First write +, – or ?. Then fill in the right form.

(play/played) Emma _____ volleyball on the beach. +

(stay/stayed) Emma didn't _____ at home

(go/went) Did Caroline _____ to a drama workshop

(visit/visited) Rajiv _____ his uncle

(work/worked) Gillian didn't _____ in her holidays

(have/had) Did you _____ fun

(are/were) Charlie thinks his holidays _____ boring

7 Questions

Emma's friends want to know everything about her holidays. Here is what she said. Write down the friends' questions. You can look at TB A8 for help.

Where …?
How long …?
Where …?
What …?
What …?

(1) I went to Turkey for my holidays.

(2) We stayed for two weeks.

(3) We stayed in a holiday apartment. It was really nice.

(4) We went swimming every day and I often played volleyball. One day we went to Pamukkale.

(5) The weather was great. We had a lot of sun and it was very hot.

1. *Where did you go for your holidays* ?
2. _____ ?
3. _____ ?
4. _____ ?
5. _____ ?

After the holidays 1

8 Weather words

a) Work with a partner. Look at the weather words and read out four of them. Your partner writes them down. Are they correct? Now it is your partner's turn to read.

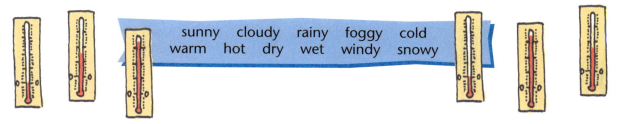

sunny   cloudy   rainy   foggy   cold
warm   hot   dry   wet   windy   snowy

b) How do **you** feel about the weather? Write the words in these lists:

Weather I like ☺	Weather I don't like ☹

c) Can you say why?

I	like don't like	rainy weather warm weather … … … … …	because I	can can't	play on my computer. play outside. go swimming. watch TV. make a snowman. go out with my dog. ride my skateboard. …

Did you know …?

The world's fastest roller coaster is the Kingda Ka in Jackson, New Jersey (USA). It has a top speed of 128mph.* Cars drive that fast on the motorway.

*mph (=miles per hour): 1mph = 1.6 km/h

1 After the holidays

9 Sound check

a) What are the weather words? Write them down.

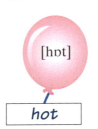     

[hɒt] — hot

['wɪndi]

[wet]

['reɪni]

['fɒgi]

['sʌni]

b) Now listen and check.

10 David's holidays

a) Listen to TB B1 again. Find the correct order and write numbers.
But: Two sentences are not from David's story.

☐ On top of Mount Snowdon it was very windy.
☐ Then they went to the train station and waited for the train to Mount Snowdon.
☐ At Caernarfon Castle it started to rain.
☐ David and his family visited Caernarfon Castle.
☐ Hoover was tired.
☐ David's father looked at a long Welsh name.
☐ On the train they had sandwiches.

b) Now write down the sentences next to the pictures.

1. _____

2. _____

3. _____

4. _____

5. _____

After the holidays 1

11 Words

TOOK DID MET STAYED BROUGHT VISITED WAS WORKED WENT WERE HAD PLAYED RAN ATE

a) Find the simple past forms for these words in the snake:

1. I take – I _took_
2. he is – he _____
3. we play – we _____
4. they visit – they _____
5. you have – you _____
6. I stay – I _____
7. we are – we _____
8. she meets – she _____
9. you go – you _____
10. they do – they _____
11. we work – we _____
12. she eats – she _____
13. we run – we _____
14. they bring – they _____

b) Can you put the simple past forms in these lists?

regular (-ed)	irregular
stayed	brought

c) Choose six of the past tense forms. Write about what you did last week.

I had a sandwich for breakfast on Monday. On Tuesday …

12 Verb tennis

Play 'verb tennis'.
Make two teams. A member of team A starts with a verb in the simple present: "I am" and throws a soft ball to a member of team B. He/She must answer with the simple past form of the verb: "I was". Team B gets one point for a correct answer. Now it's team B's turn.

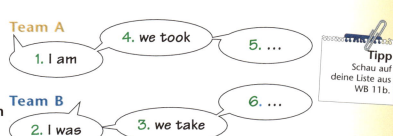

Team A: 1. I am, 4. we took, 5. …
Team B: 2. I was, 3. we take, 6. …

Tipp
Schau auf deine Liste aus WB 11b.

1 After the holidays

13 A postcard

Complete Emma's postcard to Gillian.

Hi Gillian,

This is our last day in Bodrum. It (is) __was__ very hot here. Yesterday we (go) _____ to a great beach and I (go) _____ swimming with my dad. I really (have) _____ a lot of fun here in Turkey. I (play) _____ volleyball with my new friends every day. Last week I (read) _____ a Turkish girls' magazine. You can have it when I'm back in London!

Love, Emma

Gillian Collins
49 Blenheim Crescent
London W11 1NN
Great Britain

14 Caroline's postcard

Tipp
Wenn du dir nicht ganz sicher bist, kannst du im TB auf S. 24 nachlesen.

a) Caroline wants to write to James. This is what she knows about him.

1. James' last name is Hayman.
2. He lives at 10, Sherwood Road.
3. He lives in Norwich.
4. The postcode is NR4 6AB.

Write down James' address:

b) Put the sentences in the right order. Write Caroline's postcard.

- I had science, but it was really boring!
- Please write back.
- How are you?
- I'm back in Hendon.
- Hi James!
- Today was our first day at school.
- Love, Caroline

After the holidays 1

15 Hi …!

Look at Emma's and Caroline's postcards again. Now write a postcard to **your** friend. Decorate it and put it in your portfolio.

portfolio

How to … write

16 Where are they?

Write the names of the pupils on their desks.

- Oliver doesn't like Alex and sits next to the door in front of Helen.

- Tim sits at the front, on the right.

- Alex sits next to the window. He sits behind Patsy.

- John is at the back, on the left, next to Kevin.

- Jessica sits at the front.

And where is Jenny?

_____

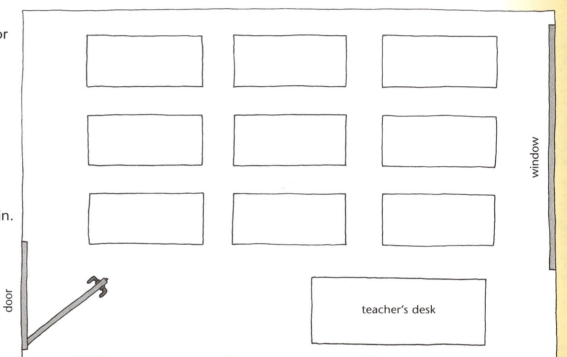

17 Describe it

Find an adjective for both* things. You can check your answers with a mirror.   *beide*

1. _____soft_____

2. _____

3. _____

4. _____

5. _____

6. _____

soft   square   hard   green   oval   round

1 After the holidays

18 Find the right picture

First look at the pictures. Then listen to the CD. Tick ✔ the right picture.

A ☐   B ☐   C ☐

19 Say it in English

Was kannst du im Englischen sagen, wenn du …

> Cheer up! – Hurry up! – I fancy him/her. – It was fun!
> I can't believe it! – What do you think about it?

jemanden aufmuntern willst: _____

sagen willst, dass etwas Spaß gemacht hat: _____

jemandem sagen willst, dass er/sie sich beeilen soll: _____

sagen willst, dass du jemanden gut findest: _____

jemanden nach seiner Meinung fragen willst: _____

sagen willst, dass du etwas nicht glauben kannst: _____

20 Find the words

Tipp
Aufgepasst! Manche Wörter werden auseinander geschrieben.

a) Find the words about holidays and school. Circle every second letter to find the word.

a b m e f a t c o h _beach_

a d o e y s p k _____

s b r o m o l k _____

c t s e n a b c l h o e p r _____

o f g e c l l t o t q i r p _____

p s u w a i r m _____

e b s o m a l r u d _____

w r e u t l l e f r _____

z c h a j l t c v u b l x a l t s o a r _____

g p l l r a f y _____

s p e o g n a y r c b a a m s p _____

f p x e f n a c o i t l z c l a f s p e _____

b) Put the words into the lists.

holidays	school

After the holidays 1

21 Caroline and James

**Gillian is asking Caroline about James, the boy she met on holiday.
Listen to the girls and tick ✔ the right answer.**

1. Caroline met James
   - [ ] on the beach.
   - [ ] in Spain.
   - [ ] at the pony camp.

2. James is from
   - [ ] Brighton.
   - [ ] Norwich.
   - [ ] Liverpool.

3. His father is
   - [ ] a detective
   - [ ] a quizmaster.
   - [ ] a teacher.

4. He goes to
   - [ ] a boys' school.
   - [ ] a girls' school.
   - [ ] a school for boys and girls.

5. At school he is in
   - [ ] year 10.
   - [ ] year 6.
   - [ ] year 9.

6. His favourite sport is
   - [ ] badminton.
   - [ ] tennis.
   - [ ] hockey.

7. His hobbies are
   - [ ] watching TV and reading.
   - [ ] reading and hip hop.
   - [ ] drawing and reading.

8. He has a
   - [ ] rabbit
   - [ ] budgie.
   - [ ] dog.

22 A guessing game

a) Emma and Caroline play this game at school. Emma thinks of a famous person and Caroline has to guess him/her. Find her questions. These words can help you:

> Is it …? – How old …? – Does he/she … ? – Is he/she …?

Is it a man or a woman _____ ? – It's a man.

_____ ? – He's 30, I think.

_____ ? – He has blond hair.

_____ ? – No, he is a sportsman.

_____ ? – Yes, he plays football.

_____ ? – Yes, he's OK.

_____ ? – Yes, it's David Beckham.

b) Work with a partner. Think of a famous person. Can your partner guess who he/she is? Change roles.

Tipp
Such dir eine Person aus, über die du viel weißt.

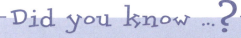

The first letter of each continent is the same as its last:
Asi**a**, **A**fric**a**, **A**ntarctic**a**, **A**ustrali**a**, **E**urop**e**, (North and South) **A**meric**a**

1 After the holidays

23 What time is it?

Tipp
Schreibe die Uhrzeiten so:
half past ...,
quarter to ...,
quarter past ...

Look at the pictures. Write down when these people have breakfast.

1 Josephine 2 Grandma Williams 3 Mr Khan 4 Hoover 5 Rajiv

1. At quarter past six Josephine drinks a cup of tea.
2. _____
3. _____
4. _____
5. On Sundays _____

24 I can do it

Read again the yellow box on page 26 in your TB. Choose one of the sentences and show what **you** have learned.

Tipp
Ihr könnt eure Ideen erst einmal auf Deutsch besprechen.

Here are some examples – but try and find your own ideas:

- You can make a poster of your classroom and talk about it.

OR

- You can make a poem about your holidays.

OR

- ...

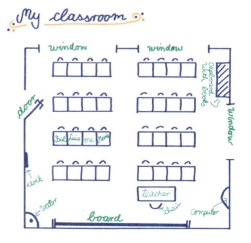

detective page 1

D1

Can you guess what these things are?

- It is hard and black. You can write on it.
- It is long and it has numbers on it.
- They know a lot of things and they give you homework.
- It tells you which subjects you have every week.

D2

How many countries can you find in theme 1? Write them down in a list. Start with the country you like best.

D3

Who says/writes these sentences in theme 1?

1. Water wet and warm. _____ (page ____)
2. I went swimming every day. _____ (page ____)
3. Oh, come on Charlie, cheer up! _____ (page ____)
4. You can't speak Welsh. _____ (page ____)
5. Hot mails to James. _____ (page ____)

D4

When do you do these things? Write down the times and draw them.

- get up
  _____

- have breakfast
  _____

- leave the house
  _____

- have a break at school
  _____

- have lunch
  _____

- do homework
  _____

- watch TV
  _____

- go to bed
  _____

2 Around London

1 Animals

Make a mindmap.

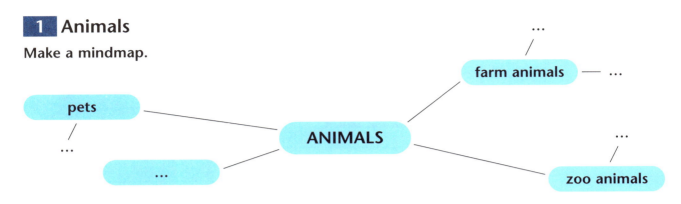

Q: How do you know there is an elephant under your bed?

A: Your nose touches* the ceiling**.

*touch – berühren; **ceiling – (Zimmer)decke

2 An exciting afternoon

Read TB A4 again and tick ✔ the correct answers.

1. Gillian is …
   - a) at school.
   - b) at home.
   - c) in the garden.

2. Her mother is …
   - a) in the living room.
   - b) at the neighbours'.
   - c) at work.

3. Gillian is …
   - a) reading a magazine.
   - b) watching TV.
   - c) listening to the radio.

4. The newsreader is talking about a …
   - a) baby tiger.
   - b) circus tiger.
   - c) tiger from the zoo.

5. The tiger isn't in its cage. Gillian is …
   - a) happy.
   - b) frightened.
   - c) angry.

6. The tiger ate its dinner at …
   - a) 3:30pm.
   - b) 4pm.
   - c) 5:30pm.

7. After its meal the tiger is always …
   - a) wild.
   - b) dangerous.
   - c) sleepy.

8. Who is trying to catch the tiger?
   - a) The keepers.
   - b) The police.
   - c) Gillian's mother.

Around London 2

3 Runaway tiger

There is an article about the tiger in the newspaper. Fill in the simple past forms.

RUNAWAY TIGER

London.

Yesterday afternoon a tiger (run) _____ away from London Zoo. It (walk) _____ in the streets of London. The keeper (go) _____ to the cage at 5pm but the tiger (be) _____ not there. The keeper (call) _____ the police. The story about the tiger (be) _____ on the radio. Many people (be) _____ frightened because tigers are wild and dangerous animals. They (call) _____ the police hotline. Finally the police (find) _____ the tiger in Kensington Gardens near the Round Pond. It (be) _____ very sleepy and they (catch) _____ it and (take) _____ it back to the zoo.

Tipp
Du kannst auch in der Liste auf S. 188–189 im TB nachschauen.

4 Who knows?

Put these words from TB A3 and A4 in the lists:

news, happy, keeper, went, orange, frightened, ate, garden, look, Asia, cage, meal, interesting, fast, catch, listen, sleepy, zoo, run, sleep

adjectives	nouns	verbs

2 Around London

5 Find the right form

Write down the present progressive forms of these verbs. Watch your spelling.

run → they	_are_ _running_	ride → he	_____ _____
rain → it	_____ _____	speak → I	_____ _____
play → we	_____ _____	swim → she	_____ _____
jump → he	_____ _____	come → they	_____ _____
sit → I	_____ _____	stop → she	_____ _____
try → you	_____ _____	write → we	_____ _____

6 Help!

The tiger is outside. A lot of people are frightened. They have a lot of questions for the police.

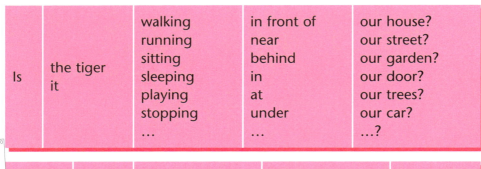

Tipp
Bei Fragen mit Fragewort senkt sich die Stimme am Ende des Satzes. Bei Ja/Nein-Fragen hebt sich die Stimme.

Make five questions and write them down.

1. _____
2. _____
3. _____
4. _____
5. _____

7 Sound check

a) The police officers want to catch the tiger. Listen to them. There are three questions. Can you find them? Tick ✔ the correct numbers.

1 ☐   2 ☐   3 ☐   4 ☐   5 ☐   6 ☐

Tipp
Achte auf die Satzmelodie.

b) Look at your questions from WB 6. Read them to a partner.

Around London 2

8 The tiger's holiday

What does the tiger normally do? What is it doing now? Look at TB A5. The words in the box and the pictures can help you.

normally:
1. stay in its cage
2. look at the visitors in the zoo
3. walk around in its cage
4. eat meat
5. sleep after a meal
6. sleep in its cage

1. *The tiger normally stays in its cage but now it is running away from the zoo.*
2. _____
3. _____
4. _____
5. _____
6. _____

9 A visit from Claire

a) Look at TB B1 again. Then tick ✔ the correct box.

1. Gillian's friend Claire is in London for a week.　　true ☐　false ☐　not in the text ☐
2. Claire is from Manchester.　　true ☐　false ☐　not in the text ☐
3. Caroline and Claire went to Camden Market yesterday.　true ☐　false ☐　not in the text ☐
4. Claire bought a new T-shirt.　　true ☐　false ☐　not in the text ☐
5. Claire and Caroline had an ice cream in Regent's Park.　true ☐　false ☐　not in the text ☐
6. The friends want to go to the zoo by bus.　　true ☐　false ☐　not in the text ☐

b) Correct the false sentences.

2 Around London

10 Say it in English

Think of TB B1 again. Gillian, Rajiv, Caroline and Claire meet at Oxford Circus.

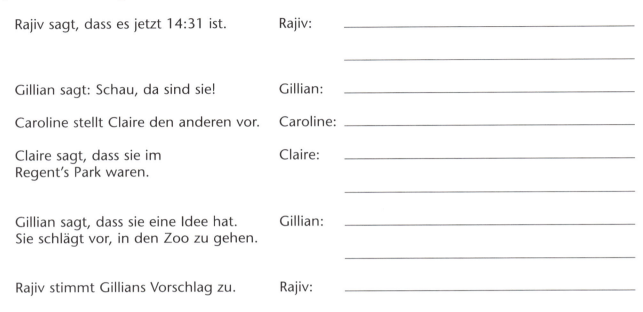

a) Write the dialogue.

Rajiv sagt, dass es jetzt 14:31 ist.	Rajiv: _____
Gillian sagt: Schau, da sind sie!	Gillian: _____
Caroline stellt Claire den anderen vor.	Caroline: _____
Claire sagt, dass sie im Regent's Park waren.	Claire: _____
Gillian sagt, dass sie eine Idee hat. Sie schlägt vor, in den Zoo zu gehen.	Gillian: _____
Rajiv stimmt Gillians Vorschlag zu.	Rajiv: _____

b) Act out what the friends say.

11 What are they like?

Find at least one animal for each adjective.

Tipp
Sieh dir noch einmal deine *mindmap* aus WB 1 an.

> dangerous   cute   small   ugly   fast   beautiful   nice
> slow   big   clever   strong   boring   interesting   …

dangerous: tiger

Did you know …?

One blue whale weighs* the same as 480 lions, or 600 giraffes, or 120,000 hedgehogs, or 480,000 mice.

*weighs – wiegen

18

Around London 2

12 Limericks

a) This poem is a limerick. Listen to the CD. Underline the lines that rhyme in the same colour.

What is a limerick, Mother?
It's a kind of poem, said brother
In which lines one and two
Rhyme with five when it's through
And three and four rhyme with each other.

b) Read this limerick. The lines are mixed up.
Put the lines in the correct order and write them down.

Tipp
Die Bilder können dir beim Verstehen des Gedichts helfen.

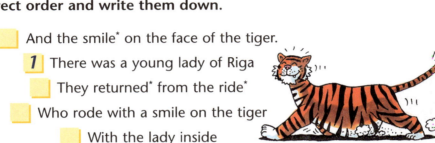

☐ And the smile* on the face of the tiger.
1 There was a young lady of Riga
☐ They returned* from the ride*
☐ Who rode with a smile on the tiger
☐ With the lady inside

© Anonymous

*smile – Lächeln   *return – zurückkommen   *ride – Ritt

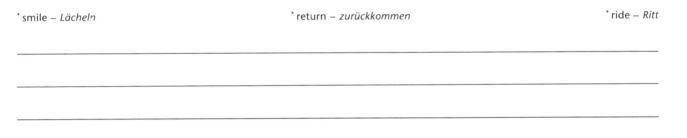

c) Listen to the CD and check your limerick.

13 What are the animals?

a) Write down the names of the animals.

1. It is small with black, grey or white fur. It has a long tail. It can run fast. It hates cats.
   _____

2. It is long and thin with little black eyes. It doesn't have any fur. People are often scared of it.
   _____

3. It has white or black fur, four legs and long ears. It lives in a cage in the garden. Its favourite food is carrots.
   _____

4. It is very big and grey. It has four legs and it lives in Africa or India. It doesn't like meat.
   _____

b) Now make a quiz for your partner.

2 Around London

14 Feeding times

a) When do these animals eat? Listen to the CD. Tick ✓ the right time.

	12:30	1:15	1:30	2:00	3:00	4:00	food
crocodiles	☐	☐	☐	☐	☐	☐	_____
chimpanzees	☐	☐	☐	☐	☐	☐	_____
spiders	☐	☐	☐	☐	☐	☐	_____
lions	☐	☐	☐	☐	☐	☐	_____
hippos	☐	☐	☐	☐	☐	☐	_____
tigers	☐	☐	☐	☐	☐	☐	_____

b) Now listen again and find out what the animals eat.
Write down the food for each animal.

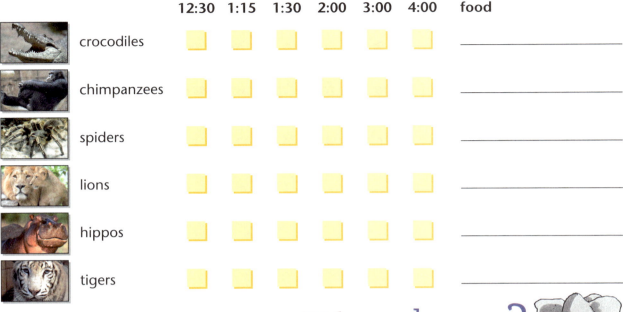

Did you know ...?
Elephants walk on their toes.

15 Excuse me. How can we get to ...?

Gillian, Rajiv, Caroline and Claire are at the zoo.
They are looking at the elephants.
Next, they want to see Rajiv's favourite animals.
They ask a zoo-keeper how they can get there.

a) Listen and draw the way on the plan with a red pencil.

b) What are Rajiv's favourite animals?

_____

c) Claire's favourite animals are the penguins.
Take a blue pencil and draw the way from the crocodiles to the penguins on the plan.
Then write it down.

Walk _____

_____

_____

d) Find your favourite animals on the plan.
Tell your partner the way. Can he/she guess your animals?

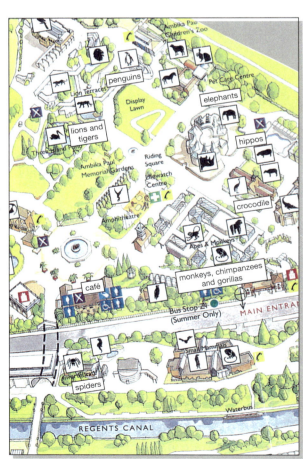

Around London 2

16 Who is who in the zoo?

a) **Here are two texts in one. There is information about penguins (underline the sentences in blue) and about elephants (underline the sentences in red).**

There are seventeen kinds of penguins in the world. Elephants are very strong and clever animals. People really like to watch them because they are very cute. In Asia elephants work hard in camps. Penguins can't fly like birds but they are very good swimmers. They use their trunks to carry things. They 'fly' through the water. When their keeper feeds them, they walk after him. At London Zoo the elephants and their keepers are good friends. The keepers wash and feed their big friends and they clean their teeth and feet. They can be between 68 and 70 cm tall. The keepers take the elephants for long walks around the zoo. Many baby penguins are born in London Zoo and many of them find a home in a different zoo. And sometimes they let their keepers ride on their backs.

b) **Choose one animal and write down the sentences. Then find a title for your text and write it on the first line.**

_____

_____
_____
_____
_____

Tipp
Überprüfe auch, ob der Text komplett ist.

c) **Give your text to a partner. He/She checks the spelling. Check your partner's text.**

17 London Zoo

Look again at the brochure in TB B10. Fill in the right numbers.

| 12,000 | 1827 | 20 | 1,500 | 3,000 | 100 | 6,000 |

1. Food for an elephant costs £_____.

2. Many of the _____ animals in London Zoo were born in zoos.

3. Food for a giraffe costs £_____.

4. For £_____ you can adopt a small animal.

5. Food for a tiger costs £_____.

6. An elephant drinks _____ litres of water.

7. London Zoo opened its doors in _____.

2 Around London

18 A London puzzle

Find the sights and write the letters in the boxes. Look at TB C1 for help.

1. It is rainy today and you want to watch a new movie.
   Go to the ☐☐☐☐ ☐☐☐☐☐☐☐ ☐☐☐☐ ☐☐☐☐☐☐ ☐

2. Are you interested in animals?
   Then the ☐☐☐ is the right place for you. ☐

3. The river through London:
   ☐☐☐☐☐ ☐☐☐☐☐☐☐ ☐

4. Do you want to see an old castle?
   Then join the queue in front of the ☐☐☐☐☐ ☐

5. Where kings and queens have tea:
   ☐☐☐☐☐☐☐☐☐ ☐☐☐☐☐☐ ☐

6. The Terminator wants to say "hello" to you at
   ☐☐☐☐☐☐☐☐☐☐☐☐☐ ☐

7. Look at the ship on the river.
   Now ☐☐☐☐☐ ☐☐☐☐☐☐☐ is opening for it. ☐

8. Find out all about buses, trains and tube trains at the London
   ☐☐☐☐☐☐☐ ☐☐☐☐☐☐ ☐

9. Do you want to have fun outside on a sunny day?
   Then sit in a boat in ☐☐☐☐☐☐☐☐☐ ☐

10. A round place in London with a lot of cars, buses, taxis and people:
    ☐☐☐☐☐☐☐☐☐ ☐☐☐☐☐☐☐ ☐

11. Feel like a bird and see London from 135 metres up in the sky at the
    ☐☐☐☐☐☐ ☐☐☐ ☐

12. This clock is famous for its song:
    ☐☐☐ ☐☐☐ ☐

Tipp
Die Lösung ist der Name einer Sehenswürdigkeit.

19 Sound check

a) What are these sights in London? Write them down.

1 [ˌbɪg ˈben]
2 [ˌmædm tʊˈsɔːdz]
3 [ˌtaʊər əv ˈlʌndən]
4 [biːefˌaɪ]
5 [ˌbʌkɪŋəm ˈpæləs]

b) Listen to the CD and check.

Around London 2

20 A musical

Du verbringst mit einigen deutschen Freunden ein Wochenende in London. Ihr wollt euch ein Musical anschauen. Deine Freunde sprechen nicht so gut Englisch wie du.

Erkläre deinen Freunden
- wie das Musical heißt
- worum es geht
- um wie viel Uhr es samstags beginnt
- was es kostet, wenn man in einer „Box" (Loge) sitzen möchte
- wie viele Personen als Gruppe zählen

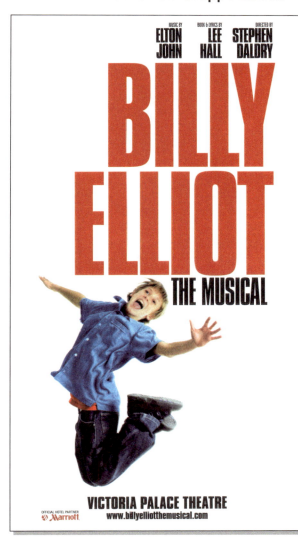

21 Odd one out

Find the odd one out.

a) king – tourist – pop star – photo – zoo-keeper
b) carrots – plants – meat – grass – apples
c) singers – actors – clowns – jugglers – music
d) lions – elephants – tigers – dogs – chimpanzees
e) park – pencil – street – shop – road
f) Madame Tussaud's – Disney Land – The Tower of London – Buckingham Palace

2 Around London

22 What did **you** do yesterday?

Walk around your classroom. Ask your classmates what they did yesterday. How many "yes" answers can you get in 5 minutes? Write down the names.

Did you …   Yes, I did.   No, I didn't.

names

… read a book?   _____

… watch TV?   _____

… go swimming?   _____

… visit a friend?   _____

… ride your bike?   _____

… meet an interesting person?   _____

… eat chocolate?   _____

Did you know …?
A tiger can tell another tiger to go left or right just by moving its ears.

---

23 I can do it

Read again the yellow box on page 45 in your TB. Choose one of the sentences and show what **you** have learned.

Here are some examples but try and find your own ideas:

- You can write/act a dialogue with a partner. Tell him/her the way (from the bus stop to school/from your classroom to the toilet/…).

OR

- You can make a poster about London and present it.

OR

- …

Q: Why do mother kangaroos hate rainy days?
A: Because the kids have to play inside.

detective page 2

D1
Work with a partner. Find these words in theme 2:

`_ _ e v _ _`   `_ _ _ i c e`   `_ _ t y`

`_ a s c _ _ _ _`   `_ _ _ _ o d`

`_ n a _ _`   `_ _ _ e u _`   `_ _ w e _`

D2
Fill in the missing words.

1. mouse – hole
   _____ – aquarium

2. uncle – _____
   husband – wife

3. music – sing
   story – _____

4. elephant – Africa
   tiger – _____

5. _____ – was
   have – had

6. morning – afternoon
   am – _____

7. like – hate
   win – _____

8. letter – write
   book – _____

9. car _____ – street
   _____ – river

D3
Word search:
Find these present progressive forms:

buying going sleeping eating looking
swimming flying running

G	N	I	T	A	E	R	G	G	G
S	W	I	M	M	I	N	G	N	N
R	U	N	N	I	N	G	P	I	I
G	N	I	K	O	O	L	L	Y	O
S	L	E	E	P	I	N	G	L	G
G	N	I	Y	U	B	O	Z	F	J

D4
A time quiz: Look at theme 2 again and find the times.

- When did the keeper go to the tiger's cage? _____
- When did Caroline and Claire meet Rajiv and Gillian? _____
- When do elephants have a bath? _____
- At what time do the lions get their food? _____
- What are the opening hours of the Tower of London? _____

D5
What is your favourite town/city? Why?

_____

_____

3 Dreams

1 Future alphabet

Think of your future. Can you find a word for each letter?

Tipp
Du kannst auch im *dictionary* nachschauen.

A _____	F _____	K _____	P _____	U _____
B _____	G _____	L _____	Q _____	V _____
C _____	H _____	M _____	R _____	W _____
D _____	I _____	N _____	S _____	X/Y _____
E _____	J _____	O _____	T _____	Z _____

2 At Gillian's place

Read TB A2 again. Who says what? Write the correct letter in the box.

 C

 G

 M

"You have a cat. Her name is Socks."

"She doesn't wear socks."

1. ☐

2. ☐

"I'll have a lot of fun with my friends."

"It's very dark in here."

3. ☐

4. ☐

"You will help me to bake a cake."

"I'll have a big family."

5. ☐

6. ☐

"We can't go out because it's raining."

"I won't marry anyone."

7. ☐

8. ☐

Dreams 3

3 The friends' future

Look at Gillian, Caroline and George. Write down what they think about their future.
Use *will* or *won't*.

Caroline: I think I will be a _____

_____

_____

Gillian: _____

_____

_____

George: _____

_____

_____

4 Your dreams

Answer the questions about **your** future.

What will you buy when you have your first job?

I will buy _____

When will you have your first house?

_____

What will be your first car?

_____

Where will you live when you are 25?

_____

Where will you spend your holidays when you are as old as your parents?

_____

3 Dreams

5 Life in a hundred years

What will life be like in a hundred years?
a) Work with a partner. Talk about **your** ideas.

- have computers as teachers
- live on the moon
- go to … for a holiday
- fly to the stars
- all speak one language
- have more free time
- live longer
- have robots to work at home

b) Write down your ideas.

I think people will live on the moon.

___

6 My spaceship

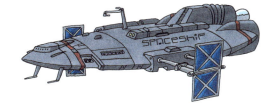

Be very quiet. Close your eyes and listen.
What do you think? What is life like on another planet?
Draw a picture and label* it. Talk about it to a partner.

*label – beschriften

7 Rap-a-dap-a-do

Make a rap about **your** future.
- Think of questions about the future.
- Work with a partner. Ask and answer your questions in turns.
  Start like this:

You:
Will I be happy?
Will I be rich?
Will I be famous?
And what about you?

Your partner:
Yes, you will./No, you won't.
Yes, you will./No, you won't.
Yes, you will./No, you won't.

Your partner: …

You: Yes, you will./No, you won't.

… …

Dreams 3

8 Sound check

a) Listen to the CD. Is it [w] or [v]? Draw lines first.

b) Now copy the word into the right list.

[v]   visit

_isit _atch _in _ideo T_ _inter _egetables _ardrobe co_er e_ening _arm _eekend

[w]

c) Work with a partner. Read the tongue twisters. Use a stopwatch. Who can read faster?

Victor, the vegetarian, ate vegetables while watching a video with William.

What in the world does this white whale want?

Very well, Sir Winston.

9 Books, comics or magazines?

a) Do you read books, comics or magazines?
Write questions. Put the words in the correct order.
Ask a partner and write down his/her answers.

book, comic or magazine/what's/favourite/your
_____?

is/what/about/it
_____?

why/you/do/it/like
_____?

b) Talk about your partner.

Tim's favourite book is … It's about …
He likes it because …

3 Dreams

10 Charlie's favourite book

Listen to Charlie. Tick ✔ the right answers.

1. Charlie's favourite book is called …
   - a) "Interesting fish."
   - b) "Beautiful fish."
   - c) "Funny fish."

2. The book has almost …
   - a) 400 pages.
   - b) 500 pages.
   - c) 100 pages.

3. Charlie likes it because …
   - a) there are a lot of interesting photos in the book.
   - b) it is very expensive.
   - c) there are a lot of exciting pages in the book.

4. There is a lot of …
   - a) fun in the book, too.
   - b) money in the book.
   - c) information in the book, too.

5. When Charlie is older he will …
   - a) draw pictures of fish.
   - b) sing about fish.
   - c) write a book about fish.

11 David's future

What's wrong here? Read TB B2 again. Underline the wrong words. Then correct the sentences.

1. David always reads a lot of books.
   _____

2. He dreams that he will be a computer specialist. Then he will have a big computer shop and sell computers.
   _____

3. Sometimes he dreams of football. His team will win the next match against Holland Park School.
   _____

4. He dreams that he will be a racing driver. He will win every race and give lots of parties.
   _____

5. When he reads comics about the past, he dreams about Robin Hood. He will be a hero and help animals.
   _____

Dreams 3

12 Jobs, jobs, jobs

What are the words?

ocrtdo _____   rngsei _____

ocok _____   pkeeozoer _____

erycrseta _____ itxa erdivr _____

eicplo icfofer _____ taceher _____

13 Who is it?

a) Match the right parts. Draw lines.

police	mechanic
zoo	specialist
car	officer
taxi	player
football	keeper
hair	driver
computer	stylist

b) Find the jobs of these people.

He/She writes letters and talks to people on the phone: _____

He/She gives concerts and sings songs: _____

He/She works at school and stands in front of the class: _____

He/She interviews people and talks about interesting things: _____

He/She works in a restaurant and cooks the meals: _____

c) Make a job quiz for a partner.

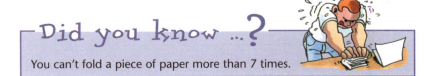

Did you know ...?
You can't fold a piece of paper more than 7 times.

3 Dreams

14 Word search

a) Write the simple present forms.

I catch – he _____   you give – she _____

we write – she _____   they repair – I _____

they look – it _____   she wants – we _____

I play – he _____   they take – he _____

you cut – she _____   she has – I _____

we do – he _____   she goes – they _____

b) How many simple present forms can you find in the wordsearch?

E	W	C	A	T	C	H	E	S
V	E	R	N	S	S	Z	T	Y
A	Q	A	I	E	K	U	S	A
H	W	R	V	T	C	O	E	L
W	R	I	A	P	E	R	O	P
O	G	T	A	K	E	S	D	L

15 Spelling championship

a) Have a spelling championship in your class. Here are some long words for you. Use a stopwatch to find the champion in your class.

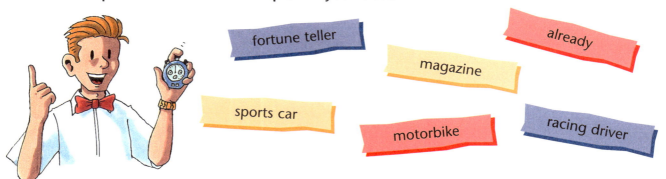

fortune teller   already   magazine   sports car   motorbike   racing driver

b) Can you find more long words with at least eight letters? Use your dictionary.

_____

_____

Dreams 3

Tipp
Du kannst auch noch einmal im TB auf S. 58–59 nachlesen.

16 A hero's story

Tell Robin Hood's story. Put the sentences in the correct order. Write the numbers in the boxes.

- [ ] The old woman told Robin Hood about the Sheriff.
- [ ] Everyone was happy again and laughed a lot about the Sheriff.
- [ ] Robin gave the old woman her clothes back.
- [ ] One day the Sheriff of Nottingham stole a lot of money from an old farmer.
- [ ] Then Robin Hood and his men brought the money back to the farmer.
- [ ] Robin Hood sent the Sheriff away without his clothes.
- [ ] Robin Hood and his men heard the farmer shout for help.
- [ ] Robin Hood and his men found the Sheriff in a woman's dress.
- [ ] The Sheriff met an old woman and took her dress.

17 Robin and Marian

Maid Marian thinks Robin Hood is wonderful. She tells her friend Lady Juliet how Robin helped the farmer. Fill in the verbs in the simple past.

LiF-Ex
3R, 4

Tipp
Überprüfe deine Lösung mithilfe der Liste am Ende des TBs.

Don't you think Robin Hood is wonderful? I think he is a very good man because he _____ (help) the poor farmer. And the Sheriff of Nottingham is really bad. He _____ (take) money from an old man! But Robin _____ (hear) the man shout for help so he _____ (go) after the Sheriff. The Sheriff _____ (take) a dress from an old woman. But then Robin _____ (meet) the old woman in the Sheriff's clothes. She _____ (tell) Robin that the Sheriff _____ (be) in the forest. Then Robin _____ (catch) the Sheriff and he _____ (give) the farmer his money. Isn't that a wonderful story? Robin Hood is my hero! He is very clever and I think I love him!

3 Dreams

18 Odd one out

a) Find the odd one out. Then find the topic for the rest of the words.
   These words can help you:

| music   jobs   body   food   ~~family~~   pets |

1. parents – uncle – sister – twin brother – ~~neighbour~~: _family_
2. sing a song – take a photo – listen to a CD – play the keyboard – practise a rap: _____
3. doctor – driver – mechanic – robot – fireman: _____
4. arm – head – nose – part – eye: _____
5. coffee – apple – banana – egg – bread: _____
6. cat – giraffe – dog – hamster – guinea pig: _____

b) Make your odd one out for a partner. Here are some ideas:

| drinks   zoo animals   school things   hobbies   … |

19 Say it in English

Look at these people. What are they saying?

| That's a great idea!   You did really well.   No, thanks. |

Tipp
Die *Say it in English*-Seiten in der Wortliste können dir helfen.

①

②

Let's go to the cinema!
③

Dreams 3

20 Kenny and Rajiv

Read TB C2 again. Write about what happens.

Kenny and Rajiv Some people The police officer They	want to go to the cinema decide to play music in Piccadilly Circus like Kenny and Rajiv's songs tells them to go have enough money can buy an ice cream	and but because so	they don't have any pocket money left. they can earn some money. they give them money. they can't play in Piccadilly Circus. they can see the film. they are really happy.

21 Monday at school

On Monday Charlie asks Rajiv about his weekend. Here are Rajiv's answers. Can you write Charlie's questions? These words can help you:

What …?   Why …?   How long …?
How much …?   Where …?

Charlie: (you – do – at the weekend?) *What did you do at the weekend?*

Rajiv: Kenny and I were buskers.

Charlie: (you – want to be – buskers?) _____

Rajiv: Because we didn't have any money. We wanted to go to the cinema.

Charlie: (you – play?) _____

Rajiv: We played at Piccadilly Circus.

Charlie: (you – play – at Piccadilly Circus?) _____

Rajiv: We played for 30 minutes.

Charlie: (you – play?) _____

Rajiv: We played our favourite songs.

Charlie: (you – money – get?) _____

Rajiv: We got over 20 pounds!

3 Dreams

22 Important jobs

Did you work last week/month/...? What did you do? Write about your jobs.

I	went shopping washed the car worked in the garden babysat	for	my dad our neighbour my grandma ...	last	Monday/ ... week. ...
	repaired my grandad's/... bike/... walked my mum's/... dog helped ... sold toys/... ...				

_____
_____
_____
_____
_____
_____
_____
_____

23 Extra money

Rajiv and Kenny played music in the street to earn some extra money.
Write down what their friends did:

1. _____
2. _____
3. _____
4. _____
5. _____

Dreams 3

24 A dictionary competition

Work in groups. Read these sentences. What are they in German? Write them down on a piece of paper. The fastest group wins.

Tipp
Schau in deinem *dictionary* im TB nach.

work with a dictionary

1. My father is a good cook.
2. Can you cook spaghetti?
3. Correct these sentences.
4. This text is correct.
5. Rajiv asks Caroline for a dance.
6. Do you want to dance with me?
7. Last night I had a funny dream.
8. Rajiv dreams about Caroline in the maths lesson.
9. My favourite drink is coke.
10. Every evening I drink a lot of milk.
11. Can you help me with my homework, please?
12. I don't understand this story. I need help.

Did you know ...?
Most people laugh about 15 times a day.

25 I can do it

Read again the yellow box on page 62 in your TB. Choose one of the sentences and show what **you** have learned.

Here is an example but try and find your own ideas:

- You can make a dialogue with a partner and talk about **your** future/**your** favourite music/ …

OR

- …

portfolio

3 detective page

D1

Find at least three jobs where people work inside and three jobs where people work outside.

inside	outside

D2

Who is your favourite person in theme 3? Why?
Write a short text about him/her and put it in your portfolio.
Try to use these words: and, but, because, so.

D3

Read these sentences. Colour them in green, yellow or blue.

- David reads comics about heroes from the past.
- Gillian will have a big family.
- We will win the football match.
- Robin Hood and his men caught the Sheriff.
- Some people listen to them.
- The farmer was happy again.

past **future** **present**

D4

Write about yourself.

When I was _____, I _____

_____

Now I'm _____ years old. I often/sometimes/always _____

_____

When I'm _____ years old, I will _____

_____

You can use these verbs or find your verbs.

play ...   eat ...   go to ...   ride ...   listen to ...   watch ...   be ...   visit ...   buy ...   have ...

Celebrations 4

1 Your interview

a) Choose some questions from TB A1 and interview your classmates. Write your questions first. Then interview your classmates and collect the number of yes-answers.

Did you let off fireworks?

Yes, I did./ No, I didn't.

QUESTIONS

Did you let off fireworks?

Did you _____

YES-ANSWERS

(names)   (number)

Lena, Patrick, Finn   *3*

b) Now write a short report about your interview. You can use these words:

> (only) three/six/… of my classmates   no one   all my classmates

_____ of my classmates let off fireworks last New Year's Eve.

Tipp
Du kannst die unregelmäßigen *simple past* Formen in der Liste hinten im TB nachschlagen.

4 Celebrations

2 Favourite festivals

Look at TB A2. True, false or not in the text? Tick ✔ the correct answer.

1. Gillian, Brenda and Samir are from London. true ☐ false ☐ not in the text ☐

2. Valentine's Day is on 14th February. true ☐ false ☐ not in the text ☐

3. Brenda's family celebrates Chinese New Year in December. true ☐ false ☐ not in the text ☐

4. Brenda's mother doesn't like Chinese New Year. true ☐ false ☐ not in the text ☐

5. Samir and his family go to the temple on Diwali. true ☐ false ☐ not in the text ☐

6. Samir gets presents for Diwali. true ☐ false ☐ not in the text ☐

3 Special days

a) What special days or festivals can you think of?
What do you need? What do you do? Make lists.

festival	what we need	what we do
Christmas	tree	give and get presents
_____	_____	_____
_____	_____	_____
_____	_____	_____
_____	_____	_____
_____	_____	_____

Tipp
Du kannst auch im *dictionary* nachschlagen.

How to ... write

portfolio

b) Read about someone's special day. Then underline the parts of the sentences you can use for a short text about your special day. Now write your text.

My birthday

My birthday is a special day. It is on 26th May and I always have a cake with candles. What I like best about my birthday are the presents. Last year my grandparents gave me a fantastic new gameboy! In the afternoon my grandparents, sisters and parents come together to celebrate. We eat the cake and they all sing "Happy birthday" for me. One of my aunts always sends me a card and some money. The weekend after my birthday is great because I have a party with my friends. But I only invite my best friends and we always have a lot of fun!

Celebrations 4

4 Festival words

Fill in the words.

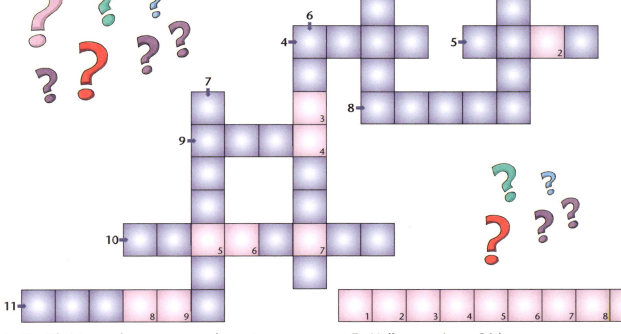

1. On Christmas day some people go to …
2. Diwali is the Hindu festival of …
3. You wear a costume for a fancy dress …
4. On Valentine's Day you send a …
5. You decorate this at Christmas.
6. You write important dates in this.
7. Halloween is on 31st …
8. … New Year!
9. On your birthday you eat a …
10. Valentine's Day is on 14th …
11. You get chocolate eggs for this festival.

5 Birthdays

What do you think of when you see the word 'birthday'?
Make a mindmap.

present

nice

give

4 Celebrations

6 Talking about plans

a) Read these sentences from TB B1 and B2. What is the same? Mark the words.

> Emma and Caroline are going to buy a present for Gillian.

> Caroline says: "I'm not going to spend £1.95 on a card."

> Are they going to buy a book?

b) Tick ✔ the right answer. You can use *going to* when you want to talk about:

a) the past (yesterday/last week/last year …) ☐
b) the present (now/today/…) ☐
c) the future (later/tomorrow/next week/…) ☐

7 The girls go shopping

a) Look at TB B2 again. Make notes.

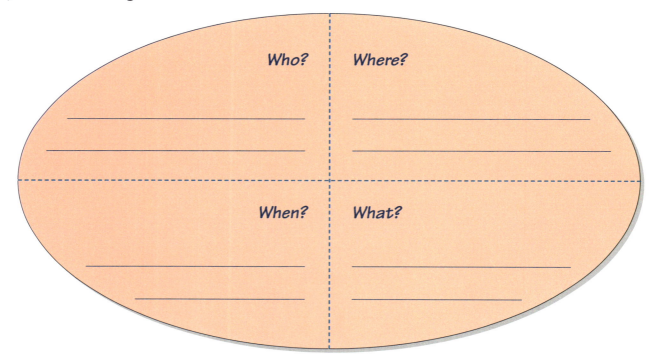

b) Match the sentences. Draw lines.

Tipp
Wenn du die Geschichte genau liest, kannst du diese Aufgabe leicht lösen.

Emma and Caroline go shopping   a Chelsea poster for Gillian.
They are going to buy   the poster is better than a card.
Selfridge's is   one of the largest department stores in London.
Caroline wants to buy   on Oxford Street.
Emma thinks   a present for Gillian's birthday.

Celebrations 4

8 At the sandwich shop

a) Listen to the people in the sandwich shop. What are they having for lunch?
Tick ✔ the right pictures.

_____ _____ _____ _____

_____ _____ _____ _____

b) Work with a partner. Write down the names of the food and drinks. Who is the fastest?

Tipp
Überprüfe im *dictionary*, ob alle Wörter richtig geschrieben sind.

― Did you know ...? ―
Dolphins sleep with one eye open.

9 Presents for everyone

a) Happy birthday! What are **you** going to give your family as a present?
You can find words for presents in the dictionary.

my mother: _____   my aunt: _____

my father: _____   my uncle: _____

my sister: _____   my grandmother: _____

my brother: _____   my grandfather: _____

my _____   my _____

b) Now talk to a partner:

What are you going to give your ... as a present?

I'm going to give him/her ...

LiF-Ex 16, 17

43

4 Celebrations

10 Different people

Tipp
Mit *as ... as ...* kannst du sagen, dass zwei Dinge/Personen gleich sind.

Look at the picture and compare the people.

tall   young   old   short

The man with the sunglasses is taller than the boy with the green pullover.

_____
_____
_____
_____
_____

11 Sound check

a) Say the words in the plural and sort them like this:

present   bike   park
dress   skirt   sandwich
bus   rose   glass
shirt   card   sock   book

[s] or [z]	[iz]
presents	roses

b) Now listen and check.

Celebrations 4

12 Charlie and Rajiv

Read TB C1 again. Answer the questions.

1. Where are Rajiv and Charlie?
   _____

2. What are they watching?
   _____

3. What can they see there?
   _____

4. What is Brenda's favourite food?
   _____

5. What did Rajiv find in the envelope?
   _____

6. What can the boys buy with the money?
   _____

7. Are they going to give the money back?
   _____

13 Chinese food

a) Listen to the CD. Write down the names of the people who call the Chinese restaurant.

   1. _____
   2. _____

b) Work with a partner. Fill in the dialogue with your names. Then read the dialogue and spell your names.

   Your partner: What's your name, please?

   You: My name is _____.

   Your partner: Sorry, how do you spell that?

   You: ____-____-____-____-____-____- …

   Your partner: Thank you.

Tipp
Das englische Alphabet findest du im TB auf S. 136.

4 Celebrations

14 What are they going to buy?

Colour the picture. Find out what these people are going to buy and who the presents are for.

1. I think the man with the ____black____ hair is going to buy a _____ for his

   _____.

2. The lady with the _____ bag is going to buy _____ for her

   _____.

3. The two little boys are _____ for their

   _____.

4. _____

   _____.

5. _____

   _____.

6. _____

   _____.

7. _____

   _____.

8. _____

   _____.

Portobello Road 2
Portfolio-Fragebögen

Name: _____

Klasse: _____

Liebe Schülerin, lieber Schüler,

vor dir liegt ein Heft mit Portfolio-Fragebögen.

Wie du schon weißt, füllst du die Fragebögen jedes Mal aus, wenn ihr ein *Theme* im Textbuch abgeschlossen habt.

Das geht so:
Sieh dir z.B. den Kasten *Hören* an. Lies die Sätze und überlege, wie gut du kannst, was dort beschrieben ist.

Hinter jedem Satz steht, wo du nachschlagen kannst, wenn du nicht genau weißt, was gemeint ist. Dort kannst du auch noch einmal üben, wenn du noch nicht so fit bist!

Vor jedem Satz steht ein Kreis mit einem Punkt ◯.

Wenn du meinst, dass du etwas schon gut kannst, dann male den Punkt und den Kreis grün aus ◉.

Du bist dir noch nicht ganz sicher? Dann male den Punkt gelb aus ◉.

Lies dann auf der angegebenen Seite im TB oder WB nach.
Kannst du es nun richtig gut? Dann male den Kreis grün aus ◉.

Wenn du noch große Schwierigkeiten hast, dann male den Punkt rot aus ◉.

Sieh dir die passenden Seiten im TB und WB noch einmal ganz genau an.
Kannst du es nun besser? Dann male den Kreis gelb aus ◉.
Wenn du es nun richtig gut kannst, male den Kreis grün aus ◉.

Auf der letzten Seite findest du einen Fragebogen, auf dem du am Ende der Klasse 6 eintragen kannst, was dir am besten beim Englischlernen geholfen hat.

Und jetzt: Viel Spaß!

Was ich nach *Theme* 1 schon kann

Hören

○ Ich kann vorgegebene Wörter aus einem Song heraushören. (→ TB S. 26)

○ Ich kann einem kurzen Telefongespräch folgen und Einzelheiten heraushören. (→ TB. S. 15)

○ Ich kann ein Bild erkennen, das beschrieben wird. (→ WB S. 10)

Sprechen

○ Ich kann etwas über meine eigenen Ferienerlebnisse und die von anderen berichten. (→ TB S. 14, 17, 18)

○ Ich kann über das Wetter sprechen. (→ TB S. 18)

○ Ich kann ein kurzes Gespräch über die Ferien, die Schule und über andere Personen führen. (→ TB S. 18, 25, 26)

○ Ich kann jetzt noch genauer beschreiben, wo sich Dinge und Personen in meinem Klassenraum befinden. (→ TB S. 24)

Lesen

○ Ich kann Ferienpostkarten lesen und mir dazu Notizen machen. (→ TB S. 14, 15)

○ Ich kann mithilfe der *wh*-Fragen verstehen, worum es in einem Text geht. (→ TB S. 17)

Schreiben

○ Ich kann eine britische Adresse schreiben. (→ WB S. 8)

○ Ich kann mit Hilfen eine kurze Postkarte schreiben. (→ WB S. 9)

○ Ich kann nach einem Modelltext einen kurzen Bericht über meine Ferien schreiben. (→ TB S. 19)

Das muss ich noch üben

Ich mache noch Fehler

Kein Problem!

Dolmetschen

○ Ich kann jemandem dabei helfen, eine englischsprachige Website eines Erlebnisparks zu verstehen. (→ WB S. 3)

Grammatik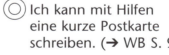

○ Ich kann erklären, wie die Vergangenheitsform gebildet wird. Ich kenne auch einige unregelmäßige Verben. (→ TB S. 21)

Was ich nach *Theme* 2 schon kann

Hören

- ⭕ Ich kann verstehen, worum es in einer kurzen Radionachricht geht. (➔ TB S. 31)
- ⭕ Ich kann einer einfachen Wegbeschreibung folgen. (➔ WB S. 20)
- ⭕ Ich kann einen Liedtext in die richtige Reihenfolge bringen. (➔ TB S. 45)
- ⭕ Ich kann mir Notizen zu einem Hörtext machen. (➔ TB S. 45)

Sprechen

- ⭕ Ich kann Tiere beschreiben und Fragen zu Tieren stellen. (➔ TB S. 30, 36)
- ⭕ Ich kann ein kurzes Gedicht auswendig vortragen (➔ TB S. 35)
- ⭕ Ich kann einen einfachen Weg beschreiben. (➔ TB S. 37)
- ⭕ Ich kann über einige Sehenswürdigkeiten Londons sprechen. (➔ TB S. 44)

- Das muss ich noch üben
- Ich mache noch Fehler
- Kein Problem!

Lesen

- ⭕ Ich kann die wichtigsten Informationen aus einem Gespräch (z.B. *Meeting friends*) oder einer Broschüre herauslesen. (➔ TB S. 31, 34, 39)
- ⭕ Ich kann Bildern kurze Informationen zuordnen, wie z.B. zu Sehenswürdigkeiten in London. (➔ TB S. 40, 41)

Schreiben

- ⭕ Ich kann einen Steckbrief über eine Person anfertigen. (➔ TB S. 34)
- ⭕ Ich kann mit Anleitung etwas über Tiere schreiben (z.B. ein kurzes Gedicht oder eine Beschreibung für das *animal book*). (➔ TB S. 35, 38)
- ⭕ Ich kann aufschreiben, was ich mir in London ansehen möchte. (➔ TB S. 44)

Wortschatz

- ⭕ Ich kann vorgegebene Adjektive und Nomen den richtigen Tieren zuordnen. (➔ TB S. 30)

Dolmetschen

- ⭕ Ich kann aus einer englischen Broschüre Informationen heraussuchen und erklären, was sie auf Deutsch bedeuten. (➔ WB S. 23)

Was ich nach *Theme* 3 schon kann

Hören

- ◎ Ich kann bestimmte Informationen aus einem Gespräch heraushören. (→ TB S. 61)
- ◎ Ich kann einzelne Wörter aus einem unbekannten Popsong verstehen. (→ TB S. 62)

- ◎ Ich kann verstehen, was jemand über sein Lieblingsbuch erzählt. (→ WB S. 30)

Sprechen

- ◎ Ich kann kurz berichten, was ich und andere gerne lesen. (→ TB S. 55; WB S. 29)
- ◎ Ich kann sagen, was ich später einmal werden möchte. (→ TB S. 56)
- ◎ Ich kann mithilfe eines vorbereiteten Posters einen Kurzvortrag über meine Zukunft halten. (→ TB S. 56)

- ◎ Ich kann jemanden nach seiner/ihrer Lieblingsperson befragen. (→ TB S. 57)

Lesen

- ◎ Ich kann Informationen über Berufe aus einem kurzen Erzähltext entnehmen und in eine Tabelle eintragen. (→ TB S. 55, 56)
- ◎ Ich kann die Handlung eines Comic (z. B. *Robin Hood*) verstehen. (→ TB S. 58, 59)

Schreiben

- ◎ Ich kann über meine Lieblingsmusik schreiben. (→ TB S. 61)
- ◎ Ich kann lebendig über mich, meine Familie und meine Zukunft schreiben. Dabei benutze ich Verbingungswörter (*and, or, but, so*). (→ TB S. 62)

- Das muss ich noch üben
- Ich mache noch Fehler
- Kein Problem!

Wortschatz

- ◎ Ich kann Wörter zu unterschiedlichen Themen (z. B. zu meiner Zukunft) sammeln und sie dann verwenden, um über mich zu schreiben. (→ TB S. 52)

Wörterbucharbeit

- ◎ Ich kann mithilfe des Wörterbuchs Verben und Nomen unterscheiden, auch wenn sie gleich aussehen. (→ TB S. 63; WB S. 37)

Was ich nach *Theme* 4 schon kann

Hören

- Ich kann gezielt bestimmte Informationen aus einem Gespräch heraushören. (→ TB S. 75)
- Ich kann verstehen, wenn jemand seinen/ihren Namen langsam buchstabiert. (→ WB S. 45)

Sprechen

- Ich kann meinen Familiennamen buchstabieren. (→ WB S. 45)
- Ich kann mithilfe von Vorgaben eine Geschichte zu Ende erzählen. (→ TB S. 76)
- Ich kann darüber sprechen, was jemand plant oder vorhat. (→ TB S. 76, 78)
- Ich kann berichten, wie in meiner Familie Feste gefeiert werden, z. B. Silvester. (→ TB S. 66, 67)
- Ich kann einen Kurzvortrag über ein Fest halten und dabei eine Collage als Hilfe benutzen. (→ TB S. 69)

Lesen

- Ich kann eine Erzählung mithilfe von Bildern lesen und verstehen. (→ TB S. 76)
- Ich kann wichtige Wörter in einem einfachen Zeitungsartikel herausfinden. (→ TB S. 77; WB S. 47)

Schreiben

- Ich kann Interviewantworten in einem einfachen Text wiedergeben. (→ TB S. 69; WB S. 39)
- Ich kann eine Einladung zu einer Party (z. B. zu einer *fancy dress party*) schreiben. (→ TB S. 78)

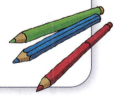

- Das muss ich noch üben
- Ich mache noch Fehler
- Kein Problem!

Grammatik

- Ich kann erklären, wie man Dinge und Personen miteinander vergleichen kann. (→ TB S. 73)

Was ich nach *Theme 5* schon kann

Hören

- ◎ Ich kann in einem Gespräch einzelne Meinungen (z. B. zu Schuluniformen oder Stars und Filmen) unterscheiden. (→ TB S. 83, 85, 90)
- ◎ Ich kann verstehen, von welchen Verkehrszeichen gesprochen wird. (→ TB S. 91)
- ◎ Ich kann verstehen, wenn jemand seine Kleidung beschreibt. (→ WB S. 56, 57)

Sprechen

- ◎ Ich kann über Regeln (z. B. zu Hause, in der Schule, im Verkehr) sprechen. (→ TB S. 84, 88, 91)
- ◎ Ich kann über meine Vorlieben sprechen. (→ TB S. 85, 89)
- ◎ Ich kann meine Kleidung und die anderer beschreiben. (→ TB S. 89)
- ◎ Ich kann sagen, wie ich zur Schule komme. (→ TB S. 92)

Lesen

- ◎ Ich kann eine E-Mail zu einem mir bekannten Thema lesen und verstehen. (→ TB S. 83)
- ◎ Ich kann verstehen, was eine englische Schulordnung vorschreibt. (→ TB S. 88)

Schreiben

- ◎ Ich kann über Regeln (z. B. zu Hause oder in der Schule) schreiben. (→ TB S. 84)
- ◎ Ich kann über Rekorde in meiner Klasse schreiben. (→ TB S. 86)

- Das muss ich noch üben
- Ich mache noch Fehler
- Kein Problem!

Dolmetschen

- ◎ Ich kann jemandem ein einfaches Spiel auf Deutsch erklären, von dem ich die Spielregeln auf Englisch gelesen habe. (→ TB S. 87)

Was ich nach *Theme* 6 schon kann

Hören

- ◯ Ich kann ein Gespräch mithilfe von Bildern verstehen. (→ TB S. 101)
- ◯ Ich kann Einzelheiten aus einem Radioprogramm verstehen. (→ TB S. 102)
- ◯ Ich kann mithilfe von Geräuschen heraushören, um was für ein Fernsehprogramm es sich handelt. (→ TB S. 103)

Lesen

- ◯ Ich kann Informationen aus einem Fernsehprogramm herauslesen. (→ WB S. 65)
- ◯ Ich kenne die *wh*-Fragen und kann damit herausfinden, was in einer spannenden Geschichte passiert ist, z. B. bei *At the museum*. (→ TB S. 104)

who? what? why? where?

Sprechen

- ◯ Ich kann sagen, was jemand tun darf, tun muss oder nicht tun darf. (→ TB S. 103)
- ◯ Ich kann über meine Fernsehgewohnheiten berichten. (→ TB S. 103)
- ◯ Ich kann sagen, was ich gern machen möchte und warum. (→ TB S. 105)
- ◯ Ich kann jemanden nach seinen Interessen befragen und über meine Interessen sprechen. (→ TB S. 106)
- ◯ Ich kann jemanden fragen, wo er/sie schon einmal gewesen ist. (→ TB S. 107)

Schreiben

- ◯ Ich kann eine Genesungskarte schreiben und jemandem gute Besserung wünschen. (→ TB S. 101)
- ◯ Ich kann eine einfache E-Mail mit einer kurzen Bitte schreiben, wie z. B einen *music request*. (→ TB S. 102)
- ◯ Ich kann mithilfe einer Wortliste einen Dinosaurier beschreiben. (→ TB S. 105)
- ◯ Ich kann eine *mindmap* zum Thema Ferien erstellen und daraus einen eigenen Text schreiben. (→ TB S. 107)

Dolmetschen

- ◯ Ich kann die wichtigsten Informationen aus einem Informationsblatt auf Deutsch wiedergeben. (→ TB S. 106)

- Das muss ich noch üben
- Ich mache noch Fehler
- Kein Problem!

Was mir in Klasse 6 beim Englischlernen geholfen hat (✓):

Hören
Hörtexte verstehe ich am besten, wenn ich
- [ ] vorweg eine Idee habe, worum es geht.
- [ ] mir beim Hören Notizen mache.
- [ ] auf Wörter achte, die öfter auftauchen.
- [ ] _____

Sprechen
Sprechen fällt mir leicht, wenn ich
- [ ] einen Dialog mit einem/r Partner/in führe.
- [ ] mir vorher Notizen mache.
- [ ] einen kleinen Vortrag halte, den ich vorbereitet habe.
- [ ] etwas mit einem Partner oder in einer Gruppe vorbereitet habe.
- [ ] etwas auswendig vortrage, z.B. ein Gedicht.
- [ ] _____

Schreiben
Schreiben gelingt mir am besten, wenn
- [ ] ich mir vorher Notizen mache.
- [ ] ich mich an eine Vorlage oder eine Mustertext halte.
- [ ] ich meinen Text später selbst durchsehen und bearbeiten kann.
- [ ] ein Partner meinen Text liest und Verbesserungsvorschläge macht.
- [ ] _____

Lesen
Lesetexte verstehe ich am besten, wenn ich
- [ ] mir vor dem Lesen Bilder und Überschriften ansehe.
- [ ] vorweg eine Idee habe, worum es im Text wahrscheinlich gehen wird.
- [ ] mir beim Lesen Notizen mache.
- [ ] auf Wörter achte, die öfter auftauchen.
- [ ] _____

Wortschatz
Wörter lerne ich am besten, wenn ich
- [ ] sie in einem Gedankennetz (mindmap) sammle.
- [ ] ähnliche Wörter zusammenstelle.
- [ ] einen kleinen Reim dazu schreibe.
- [ ] Gegensatzpaare bilde.
- [ ] _____

young – old
boy – girl
pupil – teacher
long – short

Grammatik
Grammatik begreife ich am besten, wenn
- [ ] mir jemand die Regel erklärt.
- [ ] ich die Regel selbst herausfinde und sie aufschreibe.
- [ ] _____

Das habe ich in diesem Jahr besonders gern gemacht:

_____

Celebrations 4

15 In the newspaper

a) This is the second part of the newspaper article "Chinese New Year in London." Mark the important words. Tell a partner what the article is about. The marked words can help you.

The parade starts in Chinatown in the morning. You can see many Chinese in their beautiful, colourful clothes. But they only wear these clothes for festivals, because they are very expensive. Chinese families also decorate their homes with lights, poems and flowers. Everything has the colour red. The family is a very, very important part of the Chinese New Year. Parents, children, grandparents and friends meet and celebrate together.

There is also a lot of traditional Chinese food for the festival and most families have a special meal at home. A favourite in many families are traditional shrimp dumplings. They are delicious. You can also try them at one of the many food stalls at the parade.

The festival in London this year was wonderful. There was a lot of music, lots to eat and in the evening there were fireworks. Everyone really enjoyed it. The party for Chinese New Year is great and, best of all, it's free. Everyone in London cannot wait until next year!

b) Can you now talk about
- the start of the parade • clothes • decorations • family • food?

16 Adjectives

a) Read these adjectives and write down the other forms.

nice						cheapest
		prettiest	big			
lovely			funny			
	smaller			faster		
clever			soft			
hard			late			
slow					hottest	
		coldest	good			

b) Which forms are difficult for you? Mark them in colour.

4 Celebrations

17 Say it in English

a) Was sagst du auf Englisch, wenn du …

1. wissen willst, was dein Freund/deine Freundin heute Nachmittag machen wird?

2. erzählen willst, dass du für deine Mutter ein Parfum zum Geburtstag kaufen willst?

3. möchtest, dass dir jemand den Zucker gibt?

b) Kannst du auch gute Antworten auf diese Fragen finden?

18 Odd one out

a) Find the odd one out.

cow – dog – cat – flower – rabbit – hamster

candles – cake – shop – flowers – presents – party

buy – money – shops – pay – teacher – expensive

foot – sandwich – milkshake – ice cream – cucumber

b) Make your odd one out for a partner.

_____

_____

19 I can do it

Read again the yellow box on page 78 in your TB. Choose one of the sentences and show what you have learned.

Here are some examples but try and find your own ideas:

- You can write a short poem about a festival.

OR

- You can cut out people's pictures from a magazine. Stick them on a poster. Write a text and compare them.

OR

- …

Did you know …?

The River Nile is 6,759 kilometres long. It is the longest river in the world!

detective page 4

D1

Read the stories in TB B2 and C1 and find words that rhyme with:

- me → _see_
- where → _____
- toys → _____
- sounds → _____
- sleep → _____
- eat → _____
- shop → _____
- shoe → _____
- take → _____

D2

Think about these people and compare them:

You can use these words: old   young   nice   funny   clever   pretty   tall   …

I think _____ is nicer than _____

_____ is as _____ as _____

_____

_____

_____

_____

_____

D3

A picture race. Work with a stopwatch.

1. What does the green sign in TB B2 say? _____
2. How much is the CD in TB B3? _____
3. What colour is Emma's bag in TB B2? _____
4. What colour is Charlie's pullover in TB C1? _____

D4

Who is the fastest writer? You have ten minutes to write about a festival or celebration. How much can **you** write? Count your words!

49

5 Dos and don'ts

1 Problem or no problem?

a) Look at your list from TB A1b. What are problems between you and your parents? Write **+** for "problem" and **−** for "no problem".

b) Talk about your list.

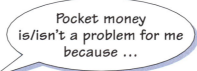

Pocket money is/isn't a problem for me because …

Rules of the house
- has to be home at 4:30pm
- mustn't wear make-up
- has to wear clean clothes
- has to do her homework
- can wear earrings
- mustn't watch TV

LiF-Ex 20

2 Rules for Gillian

What are the rules at Gillian's house? Look at the list and write sentences.

1. Gillian _____

   when she goes out with her mum.

2. She _____

   when she goes to school.

3. She _____

   from Monday to Friday.

4. She _____

   before she can go out.

5. She _____

   after nine o'clock in the evening.

6. She _____

   when she goes to see her friends.

Dos and don'ts 5

3 It's so unfair …

Read Claire's email to Caroline and find the right words for the signs. Look at TB A4 for help.

I hate my mother's rules, too. Life is so boring when you can't try new things and wear earrings or lip gloss. Why do I always !!! _____ do what she says? Some of her rules are OK. For example, I X _____ watch TV after 9pm on school days.

I + _____ ride my bike to the sports club and to my friend's house.

And I sometimes !!! _____ help in the kitchen. I X _____ eat sweets before dinner.

But why − _____ I wear make-up? And I !!! _____ wear a skirt when we go to Uncle Tom's birthday – that's terrible!

I also want to have a TV in my room and I X _____.

I !!! _____ tell my parents where I go when I go out – that's OK. But all my friends + _____ go to the youth club disco and they ☺ _____ be back by 9pm! It's so unfair.

LiF-Ex
20

4 Rules at your house?

What are the rules at <u>your</u> house? Write down what you <u>have to</u> do, what you <u>don't have to</u> do, what you <u>mustn't</u> do or what you <u>can</u> do.

1. I _____

   from Monday to Friday.

2. I _____

   when I go to see my friends.

3. I _____

   after nine o'clock in the evening.

4. I _____

   before I go to bed.

5. I _____

   when _____

5 Dos and don'ts

5 Different rules

Look at the pictures. Write down what the friends have to do.

1. Gillian wants to play football today, but she _____ _____ _____ _____ .

2. Charlie wants to play on the computer in the evening, but he _____ _____ _____ _____ .

3. Emma wants to eat fast food for dinner, but _____ _____ .

6 Let's compare

a) Complete this list.

funny – *funnier*

interesting – *more interesting*

expensive – _____

good – _____

dangerous – _____

small – _____

cheap – _____

big – _____

beautiful – _____

bad – _____

wonderful – _____

cool – _____

b) Use the words from your list in a) and write down what **you** think.

1. a monkey/a goldfish → *I think a monkey is funnier than a goldfish.*

2. my bike/your bike → _____

3. art/geography → _____

4. summer/winter → _____

5. I/you → _____

6. _____

Dos and don'ts 5

7 Gillian's dream

a) Read about Gillian's dream and underline all adjective forms.

Last night I had the craziest dream of my life:

In my dream I was shopping. I saw some earrings that were more beautiful than mine. But they were expensive. Then there was someone behind me. I looked who it was and saw the biggest chicken you can think of. It was bigger and fatter than an elephant. It was so scary! It looked like the most dangerous bird in the world. I started to walk faster and faster but the chicken had longer legs than a normal chicken and it ran after me. I didn't know what to do. The chicken was still behind me.

I ran and ran but then the street ended and there was only the canal. What should I do? Meet this terrible chicken or jump? This was the most difficult situation of my life. I jumped – and woke up.

My dreams are sometimes funny but this was the funniest dream of all. After a terrible dream like that it is the most wonderful thing to get up in the morning and go to school!

b) Write down the adjectives and add the missing forms.

crazy	crazier	the craziest

c) Now write about *your* craziest dream.

8 Sound check

a) Look at these words and say them. Then listen and say the words again.

mustn't   answer   listen   farm
talk   autumn   knee   write   know

b) In each word there is one letter that you can't hear. Find these letters and circle them in blue (mus(t)n't).

5 Dos and don'ts

9 Who's the cleverest?

a) Tick ✔ the correct answer.

1. Which is the largest ocean?
   - a) Pacific
   - b) Atlantic
   - c) Indian

2. Which is the fastest animal?
   - a) antelope
   - b) horse
   - c) cheetah

3. Which is the largest planet?
   - a) Saturn
   - b) Jupiter
   - c) Venus

4. Which is the biggest city?
   - a) New York
   - b) Sao Paulo
   - c) Tokyo

5. Which is the longest river?
   - a) Mississippi
   - b) Nile
   - c) Amazon

6. Which is the smallest country?
   - a) Vatican City
   - b) Monaco
   - c) Andorra

7. Which is the highest mountain?
   - a) Mount Everest
   - b) Kilimanjaro
   - c) Aconcagua

8. Which is the oldest underground?
   - a) the London Tube
   - b) the Frankfurt U-Bahn
   - c) the Paris Metro

You are not sure? Check here if your answers are correct.

S	C	H	E	E	T	A	H	E	B	U	T
O	L	U	A	P	O	A	S	L	A	N	D
S	O	K	W	Y	C	I	F	I	C	A	P
T	S	E	R	E	V	E	T	N	U	O	M
A	V	A	T	I	C	A	N	C	I	T	Y
N	E	R	E	T	I	P	U	J	N	O	T

b) Find more questions and ask a partner.

Which is _____?
- a) _____
- b) _____
- c) _____

Which is _____?
- a) _____
- b) _____
- c) _____

Dos and don'ts 5

10 Rhyming words

Find the rhyming words and colour them in seven colours.

BLUEBOOKNOWGREYTEAMAKETREELOOKCAKEHOUSENEWDAYBREAKTWOMOUSEHOWPLAYSHOEMECOOKCOW

Did you know ...?

You can't lick your elbow. Try it!

---

11 German school rules

You are visiting a British school and you have a brochure of your school in Germany with you. The British pupils are interested in your school rules. What can you tell them?

How to ... help out in English

Schulregeln:

- Wir verlassen das Schulgelände während der Unterrichtszeit nicht.
- Wir respektieren unsere Mitschüler und Lehrer.
- Wir können Handys mitbringen, aber nur in den Pausen benutzen.
- Schüler und Lehrer dürfen auf dem Schulgelände nicht rauchen.
- Wir werfen keine Gegenstände und Schneebälle.

5 Dos and don'ts

12 What are they wearing?

a) Listen to three pupils. They are talking about their school uniforms. Tick ✔ what they must wear at school. Do they like their school uniforms?

	Jamie	Sarah	Annabel
red blazer	☐	☐	☐
blue blazer	☐	☐	☐
green blazer	☐	☐	☐
white shirt	☐	☐	☐
grey shirt	☐	☐	☐
black pullover	☐	☐	☐
blue pullover	☐	☐	☐
grey pullover	☐	☐	☐
grey trousers/skirt	☐	☐	☐
black trousers/skirt	☐	☐	☐
black shoes	☐	☐	☐
brown shoes	☐	☐	☐
likes his/her school uniform	☐	☐	☐
doesn't like his/her school uniform	☐	☐	☐

Hi, I'm Jamie from St. Marks School.

I'm Annabel and I go to Wolvertone Grammar School.

And I'm Sarah from Winstrone High School.

b) Now colour the three uniforms with the correct colours.

13 After school

Write down what the friends do after school.

1. his fish – normally – Charlie – feeds

2. reads – David – comics – sometimes

   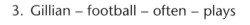

3. Gillian – football – often – plays

4. tidies – Caroline – never – her room

   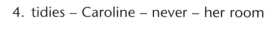

Dos and don'ts 5

14 Will's school uniform

Listen to Will from TB B5 again and look at the picture. Can you find three mistakes?

Will doesn't wear _____, _____

and _____.

He wears _____, _____

and _____.

15 Say it in English

a) These are sentences from two dialogues. In dialogue A a father is talking to his son. In dialogue B two teenagers are talking. Mark the sentences from dialogue A in blue and the sentences from dialogue B in green.

Dad, can I watch *Spiderman* on TV tonight?

Come on, let's play football!

Why don't we play basketball today?

What time is it on?

I don't know. I think basketball is OK but football is the best sport.

At 9pm.

Well, you have school tomorrow. You mustn't watch TV after 10pm.

Oh no, basketball is more exciting than football.

But *Spiderman* is such a cool film. Everybody is going to watch it …

But football players are more famous. There is David Beckham, Michael Owen …

But in the USA many NBA players are as famous as football players here.

Here's an idea: We can get the DVD for the weekend.

OK then, let's play basketball today.

Cool, thanks Dad.

b) Choose one dialogue and write it down. Act it out with a partner.

Tipp
Achte auf die Betonung der Fragen.

16 Odd one out

Find the odd one out.

1. shirt – socks – chips – trousers – skirt
2. car – taxi driver – bike – underground – helicopter
3. biggest – most beautiful – fastest – nice – smallest
4. kitchen – bedroom – door – living room – bathroom
5. play – can – must – have to – mustn't

5 Dos and don'ts

17 Signs

Look at these signs and say what you must or mustn't do.

1. _____
2. _____
3. _____
4. _____

18 Breaking the rules

Look at these pictures. Which rule is the person breaking?

1. You mustn't _____
2. _____
3. _____
4. _____
5. _____
6. _____

Dos and don'ts 5

19 Street noises

a) Listen to the noises in the street. What can you hear first? And then? Write numbers.

b) Find the words for the things in your dictionary.

_____

_____

_____

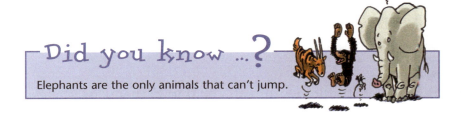

Did you know ...?
Elephants are the only animals that can't jump.

20 I can do it

Read again the yellow box on page 93 in your TB. Choose one of the sentences and show what **you** have learned.

Here are some examples but try and find your own ideas:

- You can look for a sign in your school and explain it in English.

OR

- You can make a poster about traffic rules in another country.

OR

- …

Tipp
Du kannst dir auch mit jemandem zusammen einen Dialog ausdenken.

5 detective page

D1

Think about the last two or three weeks.

What was **your** …

… nicest day? _____   … most boring day? _____

… best test? _____   … worst test? _____

… biggest problem? _____   … most delicious meal? _____

D2

Look at these animals.

Write about the animals. You can use these adjectives or find your own.

| fat | big | dangerous | fast | exciting | cuddly | peaceful | wild |
| terrible | clever | careful | funny | nice | sleepy | interesting | shy |

The hippo is the fattest animal.

_____

_____

_____

_____

D3

How many "traffic" words can you find in theme 5? Make a list. You have 5 minutes.

D4

Can you read this? What do the words mean?

HENDON SCHOOL [ru:lz]

1 Pupils must be [pəˈlaɪt] and respect the [skuːl] rules.

2 [ˈpjuːpəlz] must be in school by 8:45am.
Pupils who are [leɪt] must [fɜːst] go to the deputy head.

3 Pupils [mʌst] not [rʌn] in the school building.

Things to do 6

1 The right form

Fill in the simple past forms.

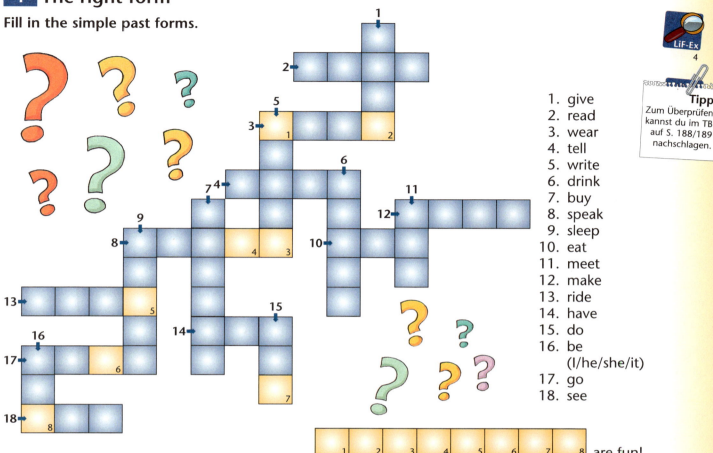

1. give
2. read
3. wear
4. tell
5. write
6. drink
7. buy
8. speak
9. sleep
10. eat
11. meet
12. make
13. ride
14. have
15. do
16. be (I/he/she/it)
17. go
18. see

Tipp
Zum Überprüfen kannst du im TB auf S. 188/189 nachschlagen.

_ _ _ _ _ _ _ _ are fun!

2 And, because, so, but?

Look at TB A2 again. Fill in the right word.

| and (3x)   because (3x)   so   but |

1. Caroline and David are going home after school _____ they are talking about their plans for the weekend.

2. David is going to the Natural History Museum _____ there is a dinosaur exhibition.

3. Emma has chicken-pox _____ she can't go out.

4. Caroline can't go to the Night Skate with Gillian _____ she is going to stay with her father.

5. Rajiv can go to the hip hop concert _____ his sister is with him.

6. Emma likes Maxx _____ she wants their new CD for her birthday.

7. Caroline and David want to buy a CD for Emma _____ the CD is too expensive.

8. Emma can read books _____ listen to the radio.

6 Things to do

3 A music request for Emma

Listen to TB A4 again. True, false or not in the text? Tick ✔ the correct answer.

1. David has sent a music request before.   true ☐   false ☐   not in the text ☐
2. Uncle Morgan lives in Manchester.   true ☐   false ☐   not in the text ☐
3. DJ Rob works at Holland Park Radio Station.   true ☐   false ☐   not in the text ☐
4. Caroline and David must tell Emma to listen to the radio.   true ☐   false ☐   not in the text ☐
5. DJ Rob will play the song for Emma in the evening.   true ☐   false ☐   not in the text ☐
6. David got a lot of 'Get well soon' cards when he had chicken-pox.   true ☐   false ☐   not in the text ☐

4 Your music request

Tipp
Ergänze deine persönliche Wortliste.

a) Put the words in the right place.

a music request can be for:
_____
_____

an ill person can have:
_____
_____

> a friend   funny   a sister   the flu   boring   a teacher   all day   chicken-pox
> interesting   a bad tooth   every afternoon   a black eye   after school
> in the evening   a mother   at the weekend   great   a brother   horrible

you can listen to a radio programme:
_____
_____

a radio show can be:
_____
_____

How to ... write

b) Now write your music request. You can use the words from a).

```
To
From
Subject
```

Dear _____,

My _____ has _____. _____ likes _____ and is a big _____ fan. Could you please play a song by _____ for _____?
_____ listens to your programme _____. Thank you!

_____

P.S.: I think your radio show is _____.

Things to do 6

5 Being ill

Look at the pictures. Write down what the parents tell their children. What can/have to/mustn't they do?

"Chickenpox is terrible."

You mustn't scratch. You _____

"I have a bad tooth."

"I want to play football with my friends."

"I really want to go to the youth club party tomorrow!"

"My head hurts. What can I do?"

6 Things to do

6 What do you like?

a) Make an interview about programmes on TV. You can ask your classmates, teachers, parents or grandparents. Ask them three questions and write their answers down like this:

1. What do you watch most often on TV? ++
2. What do you like watching? +
3. What don't you like on TV? –

name						
soap operas						
sports programmes						
music shows						
quiz shows						
talk shows						
films						
the news						

b) Talk about your results.

My friend Lara likes quiz shows best. She likes watching soap operas but she doesn't like the news.

Did you know ...?

People in Britain watch on average* 25 hours of TV every week.
'Goggle box' is another name for TV. Can you find the German word for it?

*im Durchschnitt

Things to do 6

7 What's on?

a) Look at this page from a TV magazine. Write the title for each picture.

1 _____   2 _____   3 _____   4 _____

	BBC1	**BBC2**	**Channel 4**
4pm	4.0 50/50 (T) (528) 4.30 What's New Scooby Doo? (T) (R) (4923257) 4.55 Blue Peter (T) (8984122) 5.20 Newsround Extra (T) (9343870) 5.35 Neighbours (T) (R)	4.0 Rugrats (9625726) 5.15 Weakest Link (1517287)	4.0 Back in the Day (T) (238) 4.30 Richard and Judy (T) (6693615) 5.25 Today at the Test (T) (460924)
6pm	6.0 **News** (287) (T) 6.30 **Regional News** (639)	6.0 **Flog It!** From Chelmsford. (829) (T) 6.30 **Castle in the Country** A dream castle in Wales. (981) (T)	6.0 **The Simpsons** (209) (T) (R) 6.30 **Hollyoaks** Lee and Lisa get a shock when they find their mum. (261) (T)
7pm	7.0 **Watchdog** Buying a house in Spain (8833) (T) 7.30 **Eastenders** Martin gets angry. (523) (T)	7.0 **The Good Life** Tom and Barbara try talking to their plants. (5280) (T) (R)	7.0 **News** (484218) (T) 7.55 **3 Minute Wonder** Alistair Campbell (413829) (T)
8pm	8.0 **Holby City** Owen and Diane's wedding day arrives and it doesn't start well. (2078) (T)	8.0 **Mastermind** Quiz on Judy Garland and the Beatles. (8700) (T) 8.30 **Fred Dibnah's Made in Britain** Fred shows off the wonders of the Lake District. (3385) (T)	8.0 **Jamie's School Dinners** In this new series Jamie Oliver cooks at schools. But will the pupils like his food? (36437) (T) (R)
9pm	9.0 **The life of Sherlock Holmes** A film about the world-famous detective and his friend Watson – you have to watch it! (3781) (T)	9.0 **Match of the Day Live:** England v Denmark. Gary Lineker presents coverage from the Parken Stadium, Copenhagen, as England take on the Scandinavians. (T) (83546764)	9.0 **ER** This week at the hospital: Dr. Pratt is angry with Neela and Abby has problems. (444547) (T)

b) Find answers to these questions:

1. Underline all the news programmes. How many are there? _____

2. What's the name of the film that starts at 9pm?

   _____

3. When can you watch the soap opera *Eastenders*? _____

4. *Blue Peter* is a programme for children. When can you watch it? _____

5. What is the name of the quiz show that starts at 8pm?

   _____

c) Work with a partner. Ask and answer like this:

d) Which of the programmes would **you** like to watch? Can you say why?

6 Things to do

8 A day at the museum

a) Write the questions in the correct order. Underline the question words first.

1. did – to – David – when – the – go – Natural History Museum?
   _____
2. from – he – buy – the – museum – did – what – shop?
   _____
3. sit – David – where – did – down?
   _____
4. to – spoke – David – his – dream – in – who?
   _____
5. up – why – jump – he – did?
   _____
6. who – at – David's – was – side?
   _____

b) Find the answers in TB B2.

Did you know ...?

Did you know that Britain's oldest museum is in Oxford? Its name is Ashmolean Museum of Art and Archeology. It opened in 1683 and shows drawings and paintings, silver, musical instruments, coins, clothes and other things from Europe and Egypt.

9 Odd one out

Find the odd one out.

1. small – big – long – huge – four
2. friendly – funny – walk – dangerous – strong
3. legs – teeth – head – animal – neck
4. drink – walk – sleep – eat – tail
5. ears – flowers – plants – meat – grass

Things to do 6

10 What people would love to do

Find out what these people would love to do. You can use these verbs:

| fly | be | have | go to | meet | buy |

1. Charlie would love to _____

   _____

2. _____

   _____

   _____

3. DJ Rob _____

   _____

   _____

4. _____

   _____

   _____

5. _____

   _____

11 Have you ever …?

Write down questions and interview your partner. Tick ✔ your partner's answers.

   been   gone up   baked   been   had   written

1. *Have you ever been to a zoo?* ☐ Yes, I have. ☐ No, I haven't.
2. _____ ☐ Yes, I have. ☐ No, I haven't.
3. _____ ☐ Yes, I have. ☐ No, I haven't.
4. _____ ☐ Yes, I have. ☐ No, I haven't.
5. _____ ☐ Yes, I have. ☐ No, I haven't.
6. _____ ☐ Yes, I have. ☐ No, I haven't.

6 Things to do

12 Say it in English

Wie kannst du im Englischen sagen, wenn du …

Tipp
Wenn du dir nicht ganz sicher bist, kannst du im TB auf S. 165 nachlesen.

… jemandem gute Besserung wünschen möchtest: _____

… sagen möchtest, dass eine Idee großartig ist: _____

… sagen willst, dass du jemanden vermisst: _____

… sagen möchtest, dass jemand etwas nicht tun darf: _____

… jemanden fragen möchtest, ob er sich für Sport interessiert:

_____

… sagen willst, dass du etwas sehr gern tun möchtest: _____

13 Sound check

a) Say the words and sort them like this:

| was | up | hot | shop | brother | club |
| stop | body | love | want | bus | enough |

[ɒ]	[ʌ]
was	up

b) Now listen and check.

14 I can do it

How to … write

Read again the yellow box on page 108 in your TB. Choose one sentence and show what **you** have learned.

Here are some examples but try and find your own ideas:

• You can make a poster or a poem about television and decorate it.

OR

• You can make a dialogue. Ask a partner where he/she wants to go for his/her holidays.

OR

…

detective page 6

D1

Look at theme 6 again and find words for:

1. places: _____
2. sports: _____
3. body parts: _____
4. TV programmes: _____
5. people: _____

D2

a) What can you say when you make new friends on holiday?

1. Wie sagst du, wie du heißt?
2. Wie fragst du, wo jemand herkommt?
3. Wie fragst du, wie jemand heißt?
4. Wie sagst du, wo du herkommst?
5. Wie sagst du, dass es dir hier gut gefällt?
6. Wie fragst du, wo jemand wohnt?
7. Wie fragst du, ob jemand zum ersten Mal hier ist?
8. Wie machst du einen Vorschlag?
9. Wie fragst du, was jemand gerne macht?

a) What are your hobbies?
b) Where are you from?
c) Where are you staying?
d) What's your name?
e) My name is …
f) I'm from …
g) I love it here.
h) Is it the first time you've been to …?
i) Why don't we go to my place?

b) Work with a partner. Use the sentences from a) for a dialogue.

D3

a) Think of eight funny questions. Ask a partner. The questions from WB 11 can help you.

b) Tell the class about your partner's answers

Have you ever eaten …?

Yes, I have./ No, I haven't

Have you ever been to … ?

Finn has never been to the moon. He has eaten sushi.

Have you ever seen …?

Tipp
Das Partizip der unregelmäßigen Verben findest du in der 3. Spalte im TB S. 188–189.

D4

Your second year of English with *Portobello Road* is over. Write about …

- … **your** favourite theme.
You can copy a text and decorate it.
You can also collect all the words you know from this theme.

OR

- … **your** favourite person in the book.

OR

- … **your** favourite page(s) in the book. Write what you like about it/them.

LiF in short

1R Formen von ‚be'

- Beim Sprechen benutzt man die **Kurzform**, beim Schreiben häufig die **Langform**.

Langform	Kurzform	
I am	I'm	ich bin
you are	you're	du bist, Sie sind
he/she/it is	he's/she's/it's	er/sie/es ist
we are	we're	wir sind
you are	you're	ihr seid, Sie sind
they are	they're	sie sind

- Bei der Verneinung wird an die entsprechende Form von **be** einfach **not** angehängt.

Langform	Kurzform	
I am not	I'm not	ich bin nicht
you are not	you aren't	du bist nicht, Sie sind nicht
he/she/it is not	he/she/it isn't	er/sie/es ist nicht
we are not	we aren't	wir sind nicht
you are not	you aren't	ihr seid nicht, Sie sind nicht
they are not	they aren't	sie sind nicht

2R Die einfache Gegenwart (simple present)

- Die einfache Gegenwart benutzt man, wenn man über Gewohnheiten oder regelmäßig vorkommende Ereignisse spricht. Man benutzt sie auch, wenn man beschreibt, dass jemand mehrere Dinge nacheinander tut (z. B. in einer Geschichte).
- Das **simple present** hat dieselbe Form wie der Infinitiv, z. B. *play*. Nur in der 3. Person Einzahl (he–she–it) wird einfach ein -**s** angehängt.

```
I     play    football.
You   play    tennis.
He    plays   cricket.
She   plays   hockey.
It    plays   with a ball.
We    play    basketball.
You   play    cards.
They  play    games.
```

- Endet das Verb mit einem Zischlaut oder einem -**s**, muss bei *he, she, it* ein -**es** an das Verb angehängt werden.
  You normally wash your face.
  He normally wash**es** his face.
- Einige Verben haben eine besondere Schreibweise:
  I do the cooking.   They tidy their room.
  He do**es** the cooking.   He tid**ies** his room.

3R Die einfache Vergangenheit (simple past): regelmäßige Verben

- Wenn man etwas erzählen will, was gestern, letzte Woche oder auch letztes Jahr war, benutzt man die einfache Vergangenheit *(simple past)*.
- Die Vergangenheitsform der regelmäßigen Verben bildet man, indem man die Endung -**ed** an den Infinitiv anhängt:
  I play football.   Ich spiele Fußball.
  I play**ed** football.   Ich habe Fußball gespielt.
- Bei Verben, die im Infinitiv auf -**e** enden, wird nur ein -**d** angehängt. dance → danc**ed**   like → lik**ed**

4 Die einfache Vergangenheit (simple past): unregelmäßige Verben

- Bei unregelmäßigen Verben wird die Vergangenheit nicht mit -ed gebildet. Die Formen findest du im TB auf S. 188–189.
- Die Vergangenheit von **be** hat zwei verschiedene Formen: **was** und **were**
- Die Vergangenheit von **have** hat nur eine Form: **had**

5 Die Verneinung der einfachen Vergangenheit

- Wenn du sagen willst, was in der Vergangenheit *nicht* geschehen ist, brauchst du **not** oder die Kurzform -**n't**, die an **was/were** angehängt wird:
  Emma was**n't** in Spain.   They were**n't** on holiday.
- Wenn im Satz kein *was/were* vorkommt, musst du **didn't** vor das Verb stellen. Das Verb selbst verwendest du dann nur im Infinitiv.
  Gillian got a card. → Rajiv **didn't** get a card.

6R there is …/there are …

- Wenn eine Sache oder eine Person vorhanden oder zu sehen ist, sagt man **there is**, bei mehreren Sachen oder Personen sagt man **there are**.
  There is a snack bar in Notting Hill.
  There are a lot of stalls at a street market.

7R Die Verlaufsform der Gegenwart (present progressive)

- Wenn man sagen möchte, was gerade passiert, benutzt man die Verlaufsform der Gegenwart *(present progressive)*.
- Die Verlaufsform bildet man so:
  Form von **be** (**am/is/are**) + Verb + **ing**
  I   **am**   listen**ing** to music.
  You   **are**   stand**ing** on my foot.
  It   **is**   rain**ing**.
  We   **are**   watch**ing** TV.
- Aufgepasst! Besondere Schreibweisen:
  Endet ein Verb im Infinitiv auf -**p**, -**t**, -**m**, -**n**, dann wird der Buchstabe verdoppelt: cut → cu**tt**ing
  Endet ein Verb im Infinitiv auf -**e**, so fällt das -**e** weg:
  make → making

8R Fragen im present progressive

- Ja/Nein-Fragen in der Verlaufsform der Gegenwart beginnen mit **am, is** oder **are**.
- Im Englischen fügt man bei Fragen, die man mit ja oder nein beantworten kann, eine zusätzliche Bestätigung oder Ablehnung hinzu: Yes, it is./No, it isn't.

	+	−
Is Emma doing her homework?	Yes, she **is**.	No, she **isn't**.
Are you listening to me?	Yes, we **are**.	No, we **aren't**.

- Wie bei allen Fragen mit Fragewort steht auch in der Verlaufsform das Fragewort immer am Anfang:
  What is Rajiv doing?   **Where** are they going?

what = was?	when = wann?	where = wo?
why = warum?	whose = wessen?	

9R Fragen mit Fragewort in der einfachen Gegenwart

- Auch in der einfachen Gegenwart steht das Fragewort immer am Anfang:
  When **do** you get up?
  What **does** he have for lunch?

Nicht vergessen: Bei *he, she, it* musst du *does* verwenden.

LiF in short

10R Ja/Nein-Fragen in der einfachen Gegenwart

- Ja/Nein-Fragen der einfachen Gegenwart bildest du, indem du **do/does** an den Anfang stellst.

	+	–
Do you know her?	Yes, I **do**.	No, I **don't**.
Does Charlie like fish?	Yes, he **does**.	No, he **doesn't**.

11 Fragen mit Fragewort in der einfachen Vergangenheit

- Bei Fragen mit Fragewort steht zuerst das Fragewort, dann folgt **did** oder **was/were**:
  Where **did** you go on holiday?
  What **was** the weather like?

12 Ja/Nein-Fragen in der einfachen Vergangenheit

- Ja/Nein-Fragen in der einfachen Vergangenheit bildest du, indem du **did** an den Satzanfang stellst.
- Bei der Antwort fügst du eine zusätzliche Bestätigung oder Ablehnung hinzu: **Yes, I did./No, I didn't.**

	+	–
Did you go on holiday?	Yes, I **did**.	No, I **didn't**.
Did Emma send you a card?	Yes, she **did**.	No, she **didn't**.

- Bei Fragen mit **was/were** stellst du **was** oder **were** an den Satzanfang. **Was** oder **were** werden auch in der Antwort wiederholt.

	+	–
Was Mary in Scotland?	Yes, she **was**.	No, she **wasn't**.
Were they happy?	Yes, they **were**.	No, they **weren't**.

13 Zukunft mit ‚will' – das ‚will'-Futur

- Wenn du über die Zukunft sprechen willst, benutzt du das ‚will'-Futur. Damit kann man Vermutungen, Vorhersagen oder Versprechen ausdrücken:
  Rajiv thinks he **will** be rich.
  Rajiv glaubt, dass er reich werden wird.
- So bildest du das ‚will'-Futur: **will** + Infinitiv des Verbs
- Vorsicht: **Will** sieht aus wie das deutsche Wort *will*. Aber es bedeutet *werden*, nicht *wollen*.
- Auch **will** hat eine Kurzform. Sie lautet **'ll**.
- Wenn du sagen möchtest, dass etwas nicht geschehen wird, benutzt du **will not** oder die Kurzform **won't**:
  I **won't** be a singer.

14 Fragen mit ‚will'

- Ja/Nein-Fragen mit **will** bildest du, indem du **will** an den Anfang stellst. In deiner Antwort verwendest du **will** oder **won't**.

	+	–
Will I be rich?	Yes, you **will**.	No, you **won't**.
Will they win?	Yes, they **will**.	No, they **won't**.

- Bei Fragen mit Fragewort steht das Fragewort wie immer am Satzanfang.
  What will you do tomorrow?
  Who will win the next match?

15R Satzstellung

- Der Bauplan einfacher englischer Sätze sieht so aus:

Subjekt	Verb	Objekt	
wer	tut	was	*(mit wem, wo, wann, usw.)*
I	play	football	with my friends.
			in the park.
			in the afternoon.

- Wenn man sagen will, wie oft etwas geschieht, benutzt man Häufigkeitsadverbien (*always, normally, sometimes, often* oder *never*). Diese Wörter stehen meistens zwischen Subjekt *(wer)* und Verb:

Subjekt	Adverb	Verb	Objekt	
wer	wie oft	tut	was	*(mit wem, wo, wann, usw.)*
I	always	play	football	with my friends. *immer*
	normally			*normalerweise*
	sometimes		in the park.	*manchmal*
	often		in the morning.	*oft*
	never			*nie*

- Es gibt auch andere Adverbien, z. B. Adverbien der Art und Weise (z.B. *quickly* oder *loudly*). Diese Wörter stehen in Sätzen ohne Objekt (was) nach dem Verb. In Sätzen mit Objekt folgen sie dem Objekt.

Subjekt	Verb	Objekt	Adverb
wer	tut	was	(wie)
We	ran away		**quickly**.
Rajiv	plays	the guitar	**loudly**.

16 Zukunft mit ‚going to' – das ‚going to'-Futur

- Wenn du sagen willst, was jemand für die Zukunft plant oder vorhat, verwendest du **going to**:
  Tom is very hungry. He is **going to** buy a sandwich.
- Die Zukunft mit **going to** bildest du so:
  Form von *be* (**am/is/are**) + **going to** + Infinitiv

I am (I'm)	going to	fly to Spain next week.
You are (You're)	going to	call your mother.
He is (He's)	going to	ask his friend.
She is (She's)	going to	do the shopping.
It is (It's)	going to	be a problem.
We are (We're)	going to	come back at six.
They are (They're)	going to	give the money back.

- Die Verneinung von **going to** ist ganz leicht: **not** steht immer hinter *am, is* oder *are*:
  I'm **not** going to call her tomorrow.

17 Fragen mit ‚going to'

- Wie bei allen Ja/Nein-Fragen mit *am, is* oder *are* rückt auch hier die Form von *be* an den Satzanfang:
  Are you going to come to Gillian's party?
  Is he going to buy a new car?
- Bei Fragen mit Fragewort steht das Fragewort wie immer am Satzanfang.
  What are the boys going to do?
  When are you going to come home?
  Where is he going to live?
  Who is she going to see?

LiF in short

18 Vergleichsformen (1) – ‚cheap, cheaper, cheapest'

- Wenn man eine Person oder eine Sache beschreiben will, benutzt man ein Adjektiv:
  The blue belt is **cheap**.

- Will man unterschiedliche Gegenstände oder Personen vergleichen, hängt man **-er** an das Adjektiv an und benutzt **than**:
  The red belt is cheap**er than** the blue belt.

- Beim „Spitzenreiter" einer Gruppe hängst du **-est** an das Adjektiv an:
  The white belt is the cheap**est**.

- Sind zwei Dinge oder Personen gleich, benutzt du **as … as**:
  The black belt is **as** cheap **as** the white belt.

- Achtung! Bei manchen Adjektiven ändert sich die Schreibweise:
  nice → nic**er** → nic**est**
  pretty → prett**ier** → prett**iest**
  big → big**ger** → big**gest**

- *good* und *bad* haben unregelmäßige Vergleichsformen:
  good → better → best
  bad → worse → worst

19 Vergleichsformen (2) – ‚more' und ‚most'

- Lange Adjektive (mit zwei oder mehr Silben) bilden die Vergleichsformen mit **more** und **most**. Man setzt **more** oder **most** vor das Adjektiv. Das Adjektiv selbst wird nicht verändert.
  interesting → **more** interesting → **most** interesting

20 Modalverben

- Mit **can** kannst du nicht nur sagen, was jemand kann, sondern auch, was jemand darf.
- **can** und **can't** wird für alle Personen benutzt.

  I **can** run fast.
  You **can** have an ice cream.

  He **can't** have a dog.

- **must** klingt wie das deutsche Wort *muss* und heißt auch *müssen*.

  Pupils **must** be polite.

- Du kannst **must** auch durch **have to/has to** ersetzen.
  Claire **must** go to bed. = She **has to** go to bed.

- Vorsicht! **must not** oder die Kurzform **mustn't** klingt wie im Deutschen *muss nicht*, aber es heißt *etwas nicht dürfen*.

  Pupils **mustn't** talk in class.

- Wenn du sagen willst, was jemand nicht tun muss, benutzt du **don't/doesn't have to**.

  We **don't have to** wear a school uniform.
  George **doesn't have to** help at home.

21R these/those

- **These** und **those** sind die Mehrzahlformen von *this* und *that*. **These** benutzt man, wenn man über Sachen spricht, die in der Nähe sind. **Those** benutzt man für Sachen, die weiter weg sind.

22 Der Imperativ

- Der Imperativ (Befehlsform) hat im Englischen immer dieselbe Form, egal, ob man eine oder mehrere Personen anspricht:
  Open your books, please.
- Bei der Verneinung des Imperativs stellt man einfach **don't** vor das Verb im Infinitiv:
  Don't forget your books, Charlie!

23 Die vollendete Gegenwart (present perfect)

- Du verwendest diese Zeitform:
  (1) für Handlungen oder Ereignisse, die in der Vergangenheit angefangen haben und noch nicht zu Ende sind:
  Emma **has been** at home for six days.
  (2) wenn Handlungen oder Ereignisse schon beendet sind, aber noch in die Gegenwart hineinwirken:
  David **has cleaned** the kitchen (now it is clean).
  (3) wenn du sagen willst, was jemand schon einmal, häufig oder noch nie getan hat:
  David **has** never **been** to a hip hop concert.

- Das *present perfect* besteht aus zwei Teilen:
  have/has + Partizip (3. Verbform)

- Auch beim *present perfect* gibt es Kurzformen.

	have/has	Partizip	
I	have (I've)	been	to the museum.
You	have (You've)	seen	your new friend.
He/She/It	has (He's/She's/It's)	watched	TV.
We	have (We've)	tidied	our room.
You	have (You've)	cleaned	your teeth.
They	have (They've)	made	a cake.

- Regelmäßige Verben bilden das Partizip mit **-ed**:
  clean → clean**ed**
- Die Partizipformen unregelmäßiger Verben findest du in der Liste auf S. 188–189 in der dritten Spalte:
  do → done
  be → been
- Bei der Verneinung steht **not** hinter **have/has**:
  I **haven't finished** my homework.

24 Ja/Nein-Fragen im present perfect

- Bei Ja/Nein-Fragen im *present perfect* steht **have** oder **has** am Satzanfang. Der Antwort fügt man eine zusätzliche Bestätigung oder Ablehnung hinzu.

	+	–
Have you been to Rome?	Yes, I **have**.	No, I **haven't**.
Has Emma made a cake?	Yes, she **has**.	No, she **hasn't**.

- Manchmal gibt es auch Signalwörter für das *present perfect*:
  Have you **ever** been to London? … *schon einmal …*
  I have **never** been to London. … *noch nie …*